PHYSICS AND ARCHÆOLOGY

PHYSICS AND ARCHÆOLOGY

BY

M. J. AITKEN

Research Laboratory for Archæology
and the History of Art
University of Oxford

1961

INTERSCIENCE PUBLISHERS INC., NEW YORK

Interscience Publishers Ltd., London

Interscience Publishers Inc., 250 Fifth Avenue, New York 1, N.Y.

For Great Britain and Northern Ireland:
Interscience Publishers Ltd., 88-90 Chancery Lane, London W.C.2.

MADE AND PRINTED IN GREAT BRITAIN BY
WILLIAM CLOWES AND SONS, LIMITED, LONDON AND BECCLES

PREFACE

This book describes some of the ways in which physics has been applied to archæology. It is intended both for the general scientific reader and for the student of *Archæometry*—measurements made on archæological material. The chapters have been carefully sectionalized, so that a reader may omit a part he finds too technical without fear of losing his track, and copious references to original papers have been included for those wishing to pursue things further. I hope, too, that it will be useful to the physicist who wishes to divert some of his skills to the aid of his archæological colleagues—particularly the chapters on magnetic location and resistivity surveying. It is, however, a mistake to regard the subject matter solely as 'scientific aids', for the fruits of co-operation can flow both ways: in magnetic dating, for instance, archæological evidence is vital to our knowledge of the past behaviour of the earth's magnetic field.

The emphasis of the book is on methods which produce objective, quantitative results. Thus, some powerful techniques, such as radiography, have been omitted since they are essentially extensions of the archæologist's subjective vision. This omission is not intended to belittle the expert eye—indeed it is a piece of apparatus difficult to rival—and although there are a limited number of methods from physics which are highly successful, radiocarbon dating and magnetic location for example, I do not believe there is any question of the new techniques sweeping all before them. Their evidence must take its place with the other pieces of jigsaw that the archæologist has to fit together. To do this he must know the weight to give to that evidence. A physicist is not a machine that, when fed with material, regurgitates an archæological answer acceptable without qualifications. I hope this book may help archæologists to understand those qualifications.

I am most grateful to Dr. Stuart Young and Mr. Charles Humphreys for drawing the diagrams, to Miss C. Hamilton Jackson for translating my handwriting into typescript, and to Mr. Graham Webster for lending me three of his photographs (Plates IV, VI, and VII). In so far as this book records my own work at the Research Laboratory for Archæology and the History of Art,

I would like to record my indebtedness to its director, Dr. E. T. Hall, for his invaluable help and stimulation, as well as to the staff of the Laboratory as a whole. Finally, I gratefully acknowledge that the book would not have been completed but for the sustaining flow of enthusiasm provided by W. C. Hayward, Esq.

Oxford, December 1960   M. J. AITKEN

CONTENTS

CHAPTER 1

FINDING

1.1 Introduction

Two factors make rapid *location* of remains an important aspect of archæological fieldwork today. First, the increasing cost of manual labour limits the amount of investigatory trial trenching that can be undertaken. Secondly, the rate at which modern civilization's tentacles now spread into the wide open spaces often leaves little time between the first discovery of an archæological site and its total obliteration. There is no longer the consolation that what is left undug this year will necessarily remain intact for the advanced techniques of the future.

Like an iceberg, only a small fraction of a country's archæology is visible above the surface; the rest has been buried by gradual accretion of soil to depths varying between tens of feet and a few inches. Even in the latter case there is often no surface indication until digging throws up pottery fragments. One might describe this oldest location technique of all as the 'pick and plough-share method', or as 'bulldozer tactics', for discovery of a site in this way usually results from fortuitous human interference. On the other hand many new sites have been found by deliberate visual study, either at ground level or from the air. Experience and intuition enable an archæologist to see relationships between surface features and reliefs which are often insignificant to the layman. Of course there are many sites, too, which are known by local tradition or legend, or which show themselves by obviously man-made disturbances, e.g. the circular banks and ditches of an Iron Age hill-fort.

The rôle of magnetic and resistivity surveying, to be described in Chapters 2 and 4, is in the *exploration* of an already discovered site, prior to its excavation. This reduces the amount of trial trenching to a minimum and gives the archæologist some idea of the task ahead of him. These techniques reveal the location of certain types of abnormal disturbance beneath the surface. They should not be over-estimated; they do not relieve the archæologist of the need to use his spade—but they do suggest the most fruitful spots in which to insert it.

1

A brief introduction to the magnetic and resistivity methods, and an outline of some others, now follow.

1.2   Aerial Photography

This is of dominant importance both in discovery and in exploration. Basically it is the recognition of a feature by its geometrical pattern. The visual evidence arises from *crop-marks*, *soil-marks*, and from slight differences in relief (*shadow-marks*); these are meaningless to an observer on the ground in the same way that to a man lying on a carpet the pattern is a confused blur.

Crop-marks result from different moisture conditions in the soil. The crop above a buried wall will ripen prematurely, showing up as a lightened line, while above a buried ditch the crop is richer and therefore darker in appearance. The angle of the sun, the state of the crop, and the type of crop are critical factors; in some conditions *reversed* crop-marks are seen, i.e. walls are dark and ditches light. Full exploitation of aerial photography requires careful choice of these conditions, and consequently routine military photographs are of limited value.

A feature seen on an aerial photograph is not easy to fix on the ground unless recognizable landmarks are nearby; this is particularly true of oblique shots—the most revealing archæologically. Hence for the exploration rôle it is desirable to use, as an adjunct, one of the ground location methods for pin-pointing. Equally well the ground methods can be used for confirmation where the aerial evidence is not more than suggestive. Aerial photography is most powerful for large-scale features of significant geometry; isolated features such as kilns and pits do not show up clearly and it is a fortunate circumstance that these are just the features most easily detectable by magnetic surveying.

Aerial photography was developed in the nineteen-twenties by Crawford and by Allen.   In Britain it has revealed the existence of many more archæological sites than had ever been suspected. A comprehensive account of the technique and its application has been given by Bradford (1957).

1.3   Magnetic Location

In *geological* prospecting the location of iron ore deposits by means of magnetic measurements was first used in Sweden at the end of the nineteenth century. The magnetic disturbances arising from *archæological* remains are very much weaker, and a highly sensitive instrument is required. To be of practical value speed and simplicity are essential, and when these requirements were met by the *proton magnetometer*, the technique was tried (Belshé, 1956) and found to be of great archæological importance (Aitken, Webster and Rees, 1958).

Although iron is the most obvious and powerful cause of magnetic disturbances, this is not of much archæological importance because association of iron with a feature is a comparatively rare event, even in Iron Age archæology. It was the strong *thermo-remanent magnetism* of burnt structures—and particularly pottery kilns—that suggested the application of magnetic surveying to archæology.

The thermo-remanent magnetism of baked clay has been a well-known phenomenon for many years (e.g. Folgheraiter, 1899), and the successful magnetic location of pottery kilns was to be expected. However, in the course of the first magnetic survey it was found that a number of disturbances of the order of magnitude expected for kilns turned out, on excavating, to emanate from filled-in pits. This immediately extended the scope of magnetic surveying from burnt feature detection to archæological sites in general, for nearly all cultures have dug holes in the ground for one reason or another—food storage, burial, rubbish, etc. The strength of the disturbance depends essentially on the *humus content* of the filling, and it is appreciable whether the filling has been burnt or not; the action of fire is to intensify the effect still further. This has the fortunate consequence that the greater the involvement with human activity, the greater is the efficiency of detection. Ditches are detectable too, but with less certainty because of their variable humus content. In special circumstances walls and roads show up magnetically.

The greatest drawback to magnetic surveying is the interfering effect of extraneous iron such as horseshoes, buried pipes and wire fencing. Such handicaps usually occur anywhere bordering present-day human habitation, but in open country, magnetic location is the quickest and surest of any of the methods of site exploration—as long as the geological structure is sedimentary. On igneous structures the thermo-remanent magnetism of the rock itself may be strong enough to mask any archæological disturbances.

1.4 Resistivity Surveying

Electrical resistivity measurements have been used in geological surveying for over forty years (Wenner, 1916) and for archæological work since 1946 (Atkinson, 1952). Resistivity is largely dependent on water content and one intuitively expects wide differences between stone, clay, wet soil, dug soil, sand, etc. Walls and ditches show up clearly with this technique; tombs, pits and underground cavities have also been detected.

The instruments available for resistivity measurements are more tedious in operation than the proton magnetometer. However, the drawback of interference from iron and igneous rocks is absent, though on the other hand rainfall seriously affects the resistivity measurements. In general, while some archæological features stand out sharply whatever the terrain, it is not always possible to distinguish others from small-scale geological effects.

1.5   Probing, Augering and Bosing

A sharpened steel *probe* ($\frac{1}{2}$ in. diameter, 3 or 4 ft long) can be used to detect pits and ditches cut into chalk for instance, as long as the top-soil is not too stony.

Actual samples at varying depths can be obtained with the *auger* (e.g. a 1 in. diameter carpenter's bit welded onto a shaft to which a transverse handle is added at the top). This is a useful confirmatory tool when the indications from a magnetic or resistivity survey are indecisive. Both augering and probing are open to the objection of possible damage.

When used for a primary survey, these methods, besides being slow and strenuous, have the disadvantage that the evidence is somewhat subjective. The last criticism applies also to *bosing*. The ground is thumped with a heavy rammer, and over filled-in pits, tombs and ditches a distinctive resonant note is heard, the intensified wavelength being governed by the size of the feature beneath. Bosing is successful where the top-soil is thin and firm with an unstratified rock, such as chalk, underneath.

The simplicity of these methods often leads to inadequate application. Their subjectiveness can be much reduced by covering the area according to a rigid grid system.

1.6   The Mine-Detector

This is primarily for the detection of metals but unfortunately it is not much use for archæological surveying because of its very limited range: the sensitivity falls off rapidly with depth, roughly as the sixth power, and only large objects can be detected further away than 1 to 2 ft. In any case metal is a comparatively rare archæological find. However, it can be a useful adjunct to magnetic surveying in identifying unwanted iron near the surface.

1.7 Phosphate and Pollen Analysis

Calcium phosphate is the main constituent of bone, and human occupation may lead to an enhanced phosphate content in the soil. This is detected by chemical analysis of regularly spaced soil-samples. The method was originated by Arrhenius (1931). Comprehensive applications have been made by Castagnol (1939) and Arrhenius (1955), among others.

The species of plant-life growing in archæological times can be identified by microscopic examination of the *pollen* left behind. The presence of the pollen of cultivated plants indicates the proximity of a farming community. Pollen is preserved in peat bogs and in acid soils (e.g. woodland and heathland).

1.8 Dowsing

Reports have been made of the location of archæological remains after the manner of water-diviners (see, for example, Scott-Elliot, 1958). Much hearsay evidence exists both for and against the efficacity of this technique; the author's personal opinion is that where success is not due to coincidence (on many archæological sites it is difficult to dig and find *nothing*), it represents a high degree of archæological intuition on the part of the dowser. Certainly a carefully controlled test for correlation between dowsing response and magnetic disturbance yielded a negative answer (Aitken, 1959).

References

Aitken, M. J., 1959: Test for correlation between dowsing response and magnetic disturbance. *Archæometry (Bull. Res. Lab. Archæology, Oxford)*, **2**, 58–59

Aitken, M. J., Webster, G. and Rees, A., 1958: Magnetic prospecting. *Antiquity*, **32**, 270–271

Arrhenius, O., 1931: Boden Analyse zum Dierste der Archäologie. *Bodenlehre und Pflanzenernährung*

Arrhenius, O., 1955: The Iron Age settlements in Gotland and the nature of the soil. *Vallhagar* (ed. Stenberger) **2**, Forlag, Copenhagen, pp. 1053–1064

Atkinson, R. J. C., 1952: Méthodes électriques de prospection en archéologie. *La Découverte du Passé* (ed. A. Laming), Picard, Paris, pp. 59–70

Belshé, J. C., 1956: Recent magnetic investigations at Cambridge University. *Advances in Physics*, **6**, 192–193

Bradford, J., 1957: *Ancient Landscapes*, Bell, London, 297 pp.

Castagnol, E. M., 1939: Méthode d'analyse des sols appliquée à la recherche d'emplacements anciennement habités. Institut indochinois pour l'Etude de l'Homme, pp. 191–203

Folgheraiter, G., 1899 : Sur les variations séculaires de l'inclinaison magnétique dans l'antiquité. *Arch. Sci. phys. nat.*, **8**, 5–16

Scott-Elliot, J., 1958 : Archæological detection. *J. Brit. Soc. Dowsers*, **14**,
338–339

Wenner, F., 1916 : A method of measuring earth resistivity. *Bull. U.S. Bur.
Stand.*, **12**, 469

CHAPTER 2

MAGNETIC LOCATION

2.1 Introduction

Magnetism is one of the oldest branches of Western science, and the question of the extent to which the Chinese Emperor Hoang-Ti made practical use of it in the third millennium B.C. still awaits further evidence. However, this book is not concerned with the *archæology* of magnetism but in the application of present-day magnetic knowledge, firstly, in this chapter to *locating* archæological remains, and secondly, in Chapter 6 to dating them.

The magnetic field of the earth has been used for navigation since the tenth century, and it has long been known that the compass is often misleading near a coast rich in *lodestone*. This is due to the distortion of the lines of force by the permanent magnetism of the iron oxide (present as magnetite, Fe_3O_4) in the lodestone. On land, prospectors use false compass readings—checked by reference to the sun or to the pole-star—as an indication of iron deposits.

If the anomalous readings are restricted to an area only a yard or two across then the cause is quite likely to be a horseshoe in the turf. By a very rare chance it might be an Iron Age implement some feet beneath. If this were the whole story, magnetic location would have a very limited rôle; however, archæologically-produced variations in the *condition* of the iron oxide, normally present to a small percentage in most features, can cause magnetic disturbances. The effects are too weak to be detected by compass deviation and the magnetic *intensity* (or *field strength*) is measured instead; using a proton magnetometer the intensity can be measured to an accuracy of 1 part in 100 000 with ease, and this is more than adequate for archæological purposes. The instrument is widely used for geological and geophysical surveys, the facility with which the detecting element can be towed behind an aeroplane or a ship being particularly valuable. Because of its great sensitivity, it reveals changes in geological structures, and it has general application in mineral and oil prospecting.

Before discussing the magnetic location technique, a very brief account of the earth's magnetic field is now given, followed by a semi-technical description of the proton magnetometer. Fuller details will be found in Chapter 3.

2.2   The Earth's Magnetic Field

2.2.1   *The Magnetic Elements*

If, anywhere on the earth's surface, a needle is suspended at its centre of gravity so that it can swing freely in all directions, and is then magnetized, it will take up a definite *inclination* to the horizontal and lie in a definite vertical plane. This plane is called the local *magnetic meridian*, and the angle which the needle makes with the horizontal is called the angle of *inclination, I*, or more simply, the magnetic *dip* (see Fig. 2.1a).

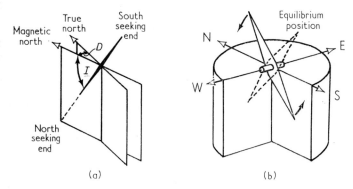

FIG. 2.1. The magnetic elements.

If the needle is now weighted so that it is horizontal, it will still take up a position in the magnetic meridian plane, and the directions defined by the needle are called *magnetic north* and *magnetic south*. The angle between *magnetic* north and *geographical* (or *true*) north is called the *compass variation*, or more commonly, the *declination, D*.

Suppose now, that the weighting is taken off the needle, and it is fixed onto a horizontal axle at its centre of gravity, the axle pointing magnetic east–west so that the needle can swing freely in the magnetic meridian plane (Fig. 2.1b). If unrestrained it will of course take up a direction making the angle of dip with the horizontal. Let the needle now be turned, on its axle, through an angle of 90°; the torque (or couple) required to restrain it from returning towards its equilibrium position is a measure of the *magnetic intensity* (or *field strength*), **F**. If the *magnetic moment* of the needle is M then the torque equals $\mathbf{M} \times \mathbf{F}$.

It is convenient to represent a magnetic field by means of *lines of force*. Their direction at any point is identical with that taken up by a freely suspended magnetized needle, and their *concentration* (number of lines per cm^2 normal to their direction) represents the field strength F. Lines of force are continuous.

2.2.2   *The Bar-Magnet Approximation*

The values of the three elements, declination (D), dip (I) and intensity (F), define the magnetic field at any point on the earth's surface. This field is approximately the same as would be produced by a short bar magnet at the earth's centre and inclined at an angle of 10° to the axis of rotation. According to this representation (see Fig. 2.2) both dip and intensity are strongly *latitude dependent*.

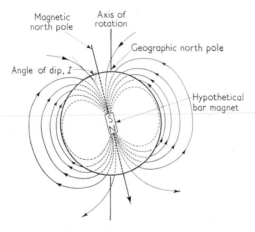

FIG. 2.2. The earth's magnetic field. The *lines of force* represent, at any point, the direction in which a small magnetized needle tries to point. The *concentration* of these lines is a measure of the field *intensity* (or *strength*).

Dip varies from 0° at the magnetic equator to 90° at the magnetic poles, while the intensity on the equator is less than half that at the poles.

For the present chapter, unless otherwise stated, it will be assumed that the magnetic surveying takes place in a locality where $I = 68°$, and $F = 0.48$ oersted. These values apply to central Britain; in North America I varies from 40° at the Panama Canal to 85° for Northern Canada, and F from 0.40 oersted to 0.61 oersted.

2.2.3   The Cause of the Earth's Field. The Secular Variation

It must be understood that the bar magnet of the last paragraph is hypothetical. The core of the earth is a hot liquid under high pressure, and the most likely cause of 99 per cent of the earth's field is the magnetic effects associated with electric currents in this liquid core. These form some sort of electromagnetic dynamo for which several sources of energy have been suggested, e.g. convection effects arising from radioactive heating or chemical separations and crystallizations.

Excluding local anomalies due to iron-ore deposits in the earth's crust and certain very small transient variations (see Section 2.2.4) the actual earth's field equals that expected on the bar-magnet model ('the *dipole* field') *plus* additional terms ('the *non-dipole* field') which in some regions reach 10 per cent of the total field. The 'non-dipole field' of the earth can be subdivided into ten regions, each several thousand miles across. It has been found that at present each region drifts westwards as a whole, on the average at the rate of 0·2° of longitude per year. This has been interpreted as the slow motion, with respect to the earth's crust, of local distortions in the current distribution near the surface of the liquid core. Together with any changes in the 'dipole field' as a whole, these effects are termed the *secular variation*. This is the basis of magnetic *dating* and does not concern the present chapter ; Figs. 7.1 and 7.2 illustrate that half-a-century is needed for an appreciable change.

2.2.4   The Transient Variations

Magnetic location depends on the detection of small-scale *spatial* variations of the magnetic intensity. Unfortunately at any given point there are also short-term *time* variations of a comparable magnitude. These are superimposed on the slow secular variation and rarely exceed 1 per cent of the total field. The changes are somewhat erratic but analysis of past records reveals daily ('diurnal'), monthly, yearly and eleven-yearly periodicities. They are attributed to variations in ionization currents in the upper atmosphere and to the arrival of charged particles from the sun. Daily and lunar atmospheric tides, variations in solar ionization, and sun-spot activity all play a part. Part (about 30 per cent) of the transient magnetic effects arises indirectly from 'eddy' currents induced in the earth's crust by the electric currents in the atmosphere.

Some transient variations are world-wide, some are localized to a region 50 miles across. On 'magnetic storm' days, significant changes (say 10 *gamma* or more) can occur in the space of 10 minutes. When surveying in such circumstances an intermittent check is made of the intensity at a fixed point, and measurements elsewhere are corrected for changes in the 'base reading'.

2.2.5 *Units*

A convenient unit for magnetic intensity (or field strength) is the *gamma*:

$$100\,000 \text{ gamma} \equiv 1 \text{ oersted (C.G.S. emu)} = 79 \cdot 6 \text{ ampere-metre}^{-1}$$
$$\text{(M.K.S.)}$$

The gamma is really a sub-unit of the C.G.S. emu system, and this system is used throughout. For convenience its relationship to the M.K.S. system is listed here:

> Magnetic induction, B: 1 gauss $= 10^{-4}$ weber-metre^{-2}
> Magnetic flux, N: 1 emu $= 10^{-8}$ weber
> Magnetization, M: 1 emu $= 1 \cdot 26 \times 10^{-3}$ weber-metre^{-2}
> Magnetic moment, m: 1 emu $= 1 \cdot 26 \times 10^{-9}$ weber-metre
> Mass susceptibility: 1 emu/g $= 1 \cdot 26 \times 10^{-2}$ M.K.S./kg.

2.3   The Proton Magnetometer (*see also Chapter 3*)

A conventional magnetometer measures the field strength by the torque which tends to turn a delicately balanced magnetic needle until it points along the lines of force. With care, instruments of this type can be made of a sufficient sensitivity for archæological surveying, but they suffer from the inherent disadvantage that levelling is necessary before measurement, and consequently the speed of operation is rather limited. The proton magnetometer, on the other hand, requires no such setting-up, and its greater speed and simplicity of operation make it vastly superior.

The proton is an elementary particle identical with the nucleus of the hydrogen atom. Its behaviour in the proton magnetometer can be understood by regarding it as a tiny bar magnet spinning rapidly about its longitudinal axis; it therefore has the properties of both a magnetized needle and a gyroscope. Because of the former it tries to point along the lines of force but its gyroscopic property prevents this temporarily and it performs gyrations while in the gradual process of achieving this direction. These gyrations are similar to those of a spinning top under the influence of gravity (see Fig. 2.3). The important thing is that the speed of

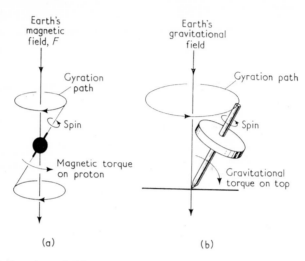

FIG. 2.3. Gyrations of: (a) a proton due to a vertical magnetic field; (b) a spinning top due to gravity.

gyration (or frequency of precession) is exactly proportional to the magnetic intensity. This frequency is about 2000 gyrations per sec for an intensity of 48000 gamma (typical figure for Britain and the southern part of the U.S.A.). Suppose it is exactly 2000·64 c/s at one measuring station, then at another station where the magnetic intensity is higher by 5 gamma the precession frequency there will be 2000·84 c/s.

Since hydrogen is a constituent part of water and of organic liquids a large number of protons (about 10^{25}) are conveniently obtained in a quarter-pint bottle and this forms the detecting element. The combined magnetic moment of gyrating protons induces an alternating voltage of about a microvolt in a coil wound around the bottle and a long flexible cable feeds this signal to the instrument for amplification and frequency measurement.

Plate I shows the instrument developed by the Archæological Research Laboratory of Oxford University. The detector-bottle is carried on a wooden tripod and moved by one operator from point to point over the area being surveyed. A second operator controls the instrument; the only action required is to press a push-button (the 'start' button) momentarily (see left-hand end of instrument panel in Plate II) and to record the digits which are indicated by

(*Ph.:* M. J. Aitken)

PLATE I. The proton magnetometer in operation. The detector bottle is carried
underneath the platform of the wooden tripod.

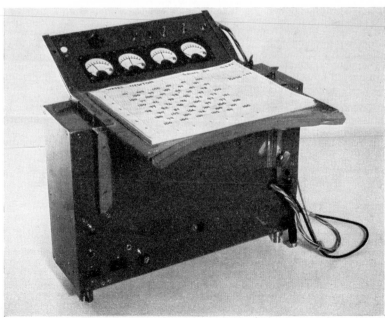

(*Ph.:* C. W. Band, Oxford)

PLATE II. The proton magnetometer—indicating meters.

the four meters some 4 sec later. The four figure number formed by these digits ('the *count*') is a measure of the magnetic intensity wherever the detector-bottle is placed. An *increase* in the magnetic intensity causes a *decrease* in the count, and 1 unit in the last digit corresponds to 1 gamma (for a total field strength of 50000 gamma). The readings are normally recorded directly in plan form and a writing board attached to the instrument facilitates this.

Each measurement involves two stages: the *polarizing period* (usually 3 sec) and the *counting period* (about $\frac{1}{2}$ sec). These are automatically sequenced by timing circuits which are triggered initially by the 'start' button. At the conclusion of the latter period the meters indicate the 'count' and this indication remains until the 'start' button is next pressed. During the polarizing period a current of 1 amp is switched through the coil around the bottle creating a magnetic field of several hundred oersteds along its axis. This ensures that there is a preferred phase at the start of the measurement, i.e. a majority of the protons point along the bottle axis. By orientating this axis roughly east–west, maximum signal *amplitude* is obtained during the subsequent counting period; at the beginning of this, the polarizing current is switched off and the protons, now freed from the restraint of the strong polarizing field, perform their lining-up gyrations as already described. The 'count' obtained indicates the *frequency* and this is *independent of bottle orientation* (as long as the amplitude of the signal is sufficient for an accurate measurement).

Since the reading of the left-hand meter (1 digit equals 1000 gamma) rarely changes during a survey, it is usually switched to monitoring the signal amplitude. During each counting period this amplitude decays, reaching one-third of its initial value in about 3 sec. The cause of this decay is two-fold: first, gradual alignment in the earth's field occurs and, secondly, the protons in different parts of the water-sample get out of phase because inter- and intramolecular fields cause slight differences in gyration frequency. Differences in gyration frequency can also arise because the *external* magnetic field is not uniform over the whole volume of the bottle. This similarly causes loss of phase among the protons and a gradient of 60 gamma per ft reduces the decay time to about 1 sec; observation of such 'fast decay' gives useful additional information (see Section 2.7).

The electrical circuits are fully transistorized and the instrument is very portable, weighing less than 25 lb. This includes built-in accumulators with sufficient capacity for a long day's work. Recharging can be very simply arranged from a 12-V automobile

(*Ph.:* M. J. Aitken)

PLATE III. The proton magnetometer—marking the maximum of an anomaly.

(*Ph.:* G. Webster)

PLATE IV. Two Romano–British pottery kilns—Water Newton, Huntingdonshire. The floor that carried the pottery is visible in the kiln on the right, and also the flue-arch, outside which the fire was lit. The kiln on the left has been partially dismantled; the central pedestal remains—this supported the fire-bars which carried the pottery-floor.

battery overnight. The main drawbacks to the instrument are the complexity of the electrical circuits and the consequent high cost (commercial models range from £750 upwards). A simplified version is described in Sections 2.9 and 3.5.

2.4   Magnetic Anomalies from Burnt Features

2.4.1   *Pottery Kilns*

The development of magnetic location was initiated specifically for the detection of *pottery kilns*. Before discussing why pottery kilns produce such a strong magnetic disturbance (or 'anomaly'), a short digression will be made as to why they are important archæologically.

Pottery *fragments* (or *sherds*), being durable and common, often form the main evidence about a site's history. The occurrence of

(Ph.: M. J. Aitken)

PLATE V. Reconstruction of Romano–British Kiln—Wattisfield, Suffolk. After loading the kiln with pottery the top was sealed over with a dome of clay, leaving holes for draught. A covering of grass was added for insulation.

(*Ph.:* G. Webster)

PLATE VI. Romano–British pottery kiln—fire-bars supported on central pedestal.

(*Ph.:* G. Webster)

PLATE VII. Abandoned pots in kiln. On excavation of the right-hand kiln of
Plate IV the pots remaining from a firing were discovered. All were slightly
faulty and it is assumed that the potter discontinued use of the kiln on that
account, and built another one.

similar types of pottery on two different sites forms a link between them, and dating evidence obtained on one can be carried over to the other—sherds are rather similar to sub-standards in physics. A pottery *kiln* is the source of these sub-standards and its excavation immediately yields geographical information about the origin of the pottery types found there. The useful life of a kiln was probably only a few years, so that if several types are found their contemporaneity will be established; in addition there is the possibility of finding a layer of complete pots left unloaded in an abandoned kiln (see Plate VII).

Besides all this, magnetic *dating* (through the same mechanism of thermo-remanent magnetism, see Chapter 7) is primarily applicable to kiln structures and hence indirectly to the associated pottery. Finally, the baked clay of the kiln can be used to give information about the past *intensity* of the earth's magnetic field which besides its intrinsic scientific interest has a bearing on the accuracy of radiocarbon dating (see Section 6.4.1).

2.4.2   *Thermo-Remanent Magnetism*

If a lump of crude clay is heated to a dull red heat and allowed to cool down in the earth's magnetic field, it will acquire a weak *permanent* magnetism. Such *thermo-remanent magnetism* is also exhibited by volcanic rocks (acquired as they cooled from the molten state) and is strong enough to produce appreciable magnetic anomalies near to lava flows. An ordinary builder's brick has sufficient thermo-remanent magnetism to deflect a compass by half a degree or more when held close to it.

The effect results from the *ferrimagnetism* (a weak sort of ferro-

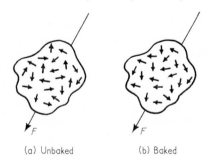

(a) Unbaked   (b) Baked

Fɪɢ. 2.4. Domain alignment in clay.

(a) Unbaked clay. Domains are in random directions and the net magnetic effect is very small.
(b) Baked clay. Elevated temperature has allowed preferential alignment which subsequently remains 'frozen' at normal temperatures.

magnetism) of *magnetite* (Fe_3O_4) and *hæmatite* (α-Fe_2O_3). The average iron oxide content of the earth's crust is 6·8 per cent, and most soil and clay, and some rocks, can be expected to contain significant quantities of magnetite and/or hæmatite. As the temperature is raised the magnetic domains* of these substances are aligned by the earth's magnetic field; on cooling again the domain directions remain fixed. Fig. 2.4a illustrates the situation in a lump of *un*baked clay by representing the domains as little bar magnets. The net magnetic effect is zero since on the average every little magnet is balanced out by another pointing in the reverse direction. Fig. 2.4b shows the situation after baking; the lump of clay can now be regarded as a very weak permanent magnet.

The ferrimagnetism of hæmatite (α-Fe_2O_3) is weak (*saturation* magnetization: 0·5 emu/g) compared to that of magnetite (*saturation* magnetization: 92 emu/g). Consequently when these minerals are dispersed in clay a wide range of magnetization can be obtained depending on the proportions, on the temperature of baking, and on the magnetic field strength in which cooling takes place. For cooling from dull red heat in the earth's magnetic field, of say 0·5 oersted, the specific remanent magnetization, σ_r, can vary in practice between 0·0001 and 0·1 emu/g of clay (for refined clays, such as china clay, relatively free from iron, the figures are very much lower). The lower limit applies to red, highly oxidized clay in which conversion of iron oxide to hæmatite is nearly complete, and the upper limit to grey reduced clay in which magnetite is predominant. Thermo-remanent properties are considered more fully in Chapter 6; the only additional point to be noted for the present is that while a dull red heat (675°C) is necessary for the maximum effect, any elevated temperature at all produces *some* effect (see Fig. 7.3).

Ferrimagnetism is exhibited by other naturally occurring minerals such as pyrrhotite (iron sulphide) and maghæmite (γ-Fe_2O_3). Only the latter, which has a saturation magnetization of 83 emu/g, has so far shown itself to be of interest archæologically (see Section 2.5.1). Although it has the same chemical formula as hæmatite its crystal structure (*inverse spinel*) is more similar to that of magnetite (*spinel*). Consequently it is much more strongly magnetic than hæmatite, which is *rhombohedral* in structure. Maghæmite converts to hæmatite if the temperature is raised above several hundred degrees centigrade.

---

* A *domain* is a minute volume of the ferrimagnetic within which the magnetization is uniform.

2.4.3   *Kiln Anomalies: Strength*

Although kilns of different civilizations may differ in construction they all have the common feature of containing, because of its
unique refractory properties, large amounts of baked clay. This
clay may be directly applied from the raw or it may be in the form
of prefabricated bricks. The amount present varies from kiln to
kiln but 1000 kilograms is a reasonable figure to assume. Taking the
range for the specific magnetization of baked clay to be 0·0001 to
0·1 emu/g, the total magnetic moment of a kiln should be between
500 and 500000 emu (taking 50000 gamma as the applied field
strength). In terms of the magnetic moment induced in average
quality iron these limits correspond to weights of a few ounces
and several hundred pounds respectively.

Because the shape of the kiln is irregular, it is not possible, in
general, to calculate the resultant magnetic field. In some types,
however, Roman kilns in particular, a substantial fraction of the
baked clay is contained in a central *pedestal* on the floor of the
kiln (see Plate IV). By assuming this pedestal to be spherical its
magnetic field may be approximated by that of a short bar magnet
having the same magnetic moment. (The field of a *uniformly*
magnetized sphere is *exactly* equal to that of a short bar magnet
of the same moment placed at its centre.)   Fig. 2.2 illustrates the
field of a short bar magnet; along the axis of the magnet field
strength ΔF is given by

$$\Delta F = \frac{2M}{d^3} \tag{2.1}$$

where M is the moment of the magnet and d is the distance from it.
Taking $M = 5000$ emu,

$$\text{for } d = 1 \text{ metre, } \Delta F = 1000 \text{ gamma}$$
$$\text{for } d = 2 \text{ metres, } \Delta F = 125 \text{ gamma}$$
$$\text{for } d = 3 \text{ metres, } \Delta F = 37 \text{ gamma}$$

The anomaly of 37 gamma represents a change in the total field
strength of 1 part in 1300, easily detectable with a proton magnetometer.

About 30 Romano–British pottery kilns have been detected
magnetically to date (1960). When the top of the pedestal is about
4 ft below the detector-bottle the anomaly usually lies in the range
100 to 200 gamma. However, this type of kiln is comparatively
substantial in construction and such strong anomalies cannot be

expected from the kilns of civilizations less advanced in ceramic technology.

2.4.4   *Kiln Anomalies: Shape*

The proton magnetometer measures the *total* field strength; this is the magnitude, R, of the *vector* resultant of the normal earth's field, F, and the additional field due to the kiln, ΔF. This is not easy to calculate because, as illustrated in Fig. 2.5, where the

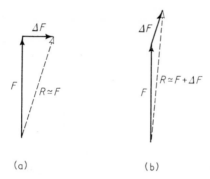

(a)   (b)

FIG. 2.5. Vector addition.
(a) Anomaly field perpendicular to main field.
(b) Anomaly field nearly parallel to main field.

direction of ΔF is perpendicular to F, R does not differ perceptibly from F, only the direction being changed.

The calculated anomaly along a north–south line passing over a short bar magnet is shown in Fig. 2.6. The distance scale (horizontal) is in units equal to the depth, d, of the magnet below the level at which the measurements are made. The ordinate scale (representing, in arbitrary units, the deviation from the normal intensity) has been inverted so as to correspond to the sense of the proton magnetometer indication. The following points should be noted.

(*a*) The maximum of the anomaly (A) lies to the *south* of the source. The displacement is approximately one-third of the depth, d.

(*b*) The separation, W, between the two points at which the anomaly has half its maximum value, is equal to the depth, d.

(*c*) The extreme of the *reverse* anomaly (B) is 10 per cent of the maximum and lies one depth unit to the *north* of the magnet.

(*d*) The anomaly is very small (less than 2 per cent) at distances greater than three times the depth, d.

Where the angle of dip is outside the range 60–70° these rules

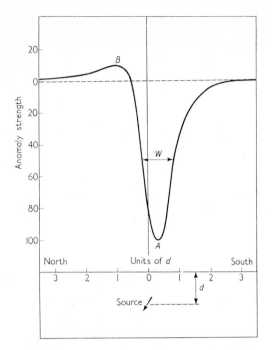

Fɪɢ. 2.6. Idealized kiln anomaly. The source has been approximated by a short bar magnet at a depth d. The angle of dip, I, is taken to be $68°$. The anomaly strength represents the deviation (in arbitrary units) from the normal field strength. The scale has been inverted so as to correspond to the proton magnetometer indication in which a decrease in 'count' corresponds to an increase in field strength.

must be modified. Fig. 2.7 shows the form of the anomaly for different angles (adapted from Smellie, 1956) and Fig. 2.8 the ratio of the burial depth to the width of the anomaly.

The foregoing discussion applies only to sources which are a good approximation to a short bar magnet, i.e. a uniformly magnetized sphere *or* a source of dimensions small compared to its distance from the detector. The effect of a more extended source is to widen the anomaly. In practice, rule (*a*) is useful but, in rule (*b*), the distance W usually represents the depth or the width of the feature, *whichever is the greater*. The reverse disturbance, referred to in rule (*c*), is often absent. The localization of the anomaly implied by rule (*d*) still holds but the anomaly is never less wide than the feature from which it emanates.

Another reason why observed anomalies differ from the ideal shape is the contiguity of a secondary one, e.g. the stokehole of a kiln may produce an anomaly for the same reason as a pit (see

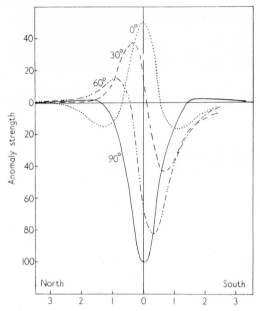

FIG. 2.7. Effect of latitude on anomaly shape. The anomalies from short bar magnets in different geomagnetic latitudes. The vertical scale is arbitrary. The horizontal scale, representing a north–south traverse through the centre of the anomaly, is in units of burial depth.

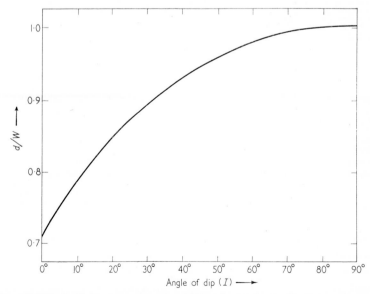

FIG. 2.8. Effect of latitude on anomaly width. d, burial depth; W, distance between points on north–south traverse through the centre of the anomaly at which the strength has fallen to half the maximum.

2+

Fig. 2.9). Plate VIII shows the kiln found beneath the lower anomaly; the bamboo marks the centre of the anomaly, note the southward displacement from the pedestal.

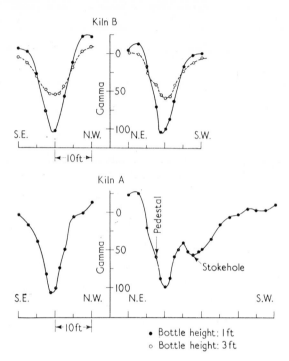

FIG. 2.9. Magnetic profiles—kilns. These readings were obtained during the survey of a Romano–British kiln site at Water Newton, Huntingdonshire. The coarse readings by which the presence of the anomalies was first detected are shown in Fig. 2.16. The curves above represent perpendicular traverses through the maximum. On excavation kilns were found, about 5 ft in diameter and with floors 4·5 ft below the present ground surface; each had a substantial central pedestal.

2.4.5 *Other Burnt Features*

The disturbance from domestic hearths, ovens, furnaces, etc. is smaller proportionally to the amount of baked clay in these features, but they are easily detectable as long as the depth of burial is not excessive.

The magnetic effect of a *burnt* feature is greatly attenuated by disarrangement. Magnetism is a directional effect and, in the same way as the random orientations of magnetic domains cause mutual annulment in unbaked clay, so too, on a larger scale but to an incomplete degree, do the constituent parts of a structure if they

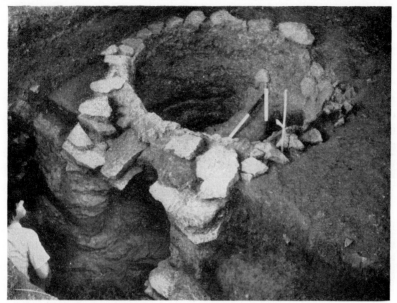

(*Ph.:* M. J. Aitken)

PLATE VIII. Romano–British pottery kiln. The bamboo (with label) has been carried down from its insertion, prior to excavation, at the maximum of the magnetic anomaly. It is several feet south of the pedestal, as expected.

have been moved since baking. The extreme case of this is a dump of pottery sherds; although the thermo-remanent magnetism of each individual sherd may be high, the net effect detected will be comparatively small.

2.5 Magnetic Anomalies from Filled-in Pits

2.5.1 *The Magnetic Susceptibility of Soils*

As recounted in Section 1.3, the strength of the magnetic anomaly from a filled-in pit was greater than expected in the absence of thermo-remanent effects. However, laboratory measurements show that the magnetic susceptibility of soil from pit-fillings can be remarkably high and sufficient to account for the order of magnitude of the observed anomalies. The *susceptibility* (per unit mass) expresses the magnetic moment *induced* in 1 gram of the sample when it is placed in a magnetic field of 1 oersted, *without any heat treatment*. The specific magnetization is obtained by multiplying the susceptibility by the earth's field strength (say 0·5 oersted).

Induced magnetization is essentially *temporary*; in whatever direction a sample is turned its magnetic moment always lies along the direction of the lines of force of the earth's magnetic field that is inducing that moment. In terms of the little bar magnets representing the magnetic domains (see Fig. 2.4) the effect is explained as a slight increase in the strength of those that happen to be pointing in the same direction as the field and a slight decrease for those in the opposite direction. This occurs instantaneously and results in a net magnetic moment. (It has been assumed here that no *re-orientation* of domains is possible at normal temperatures; such an effect is termed *isothermal* remanent magnetism, but it is small compared to the instantaneously induced susceptibility.)

The susceptibilities of miscellaneous samples of soil collected from a number of archæological sites are given in Table 2.1. With two exceptions (Arras and Dane's Camp), the susceptibilities of samples taken from the filling of an archæological feature are higher than from elsewhere. Without exception, all samples of soil have a higher susceptibility than the underlying sub-stratum. The actual degree of magnetization is in some cases comparable with the thermo-remanent magnetism of oxidized baked clay.

The enhanced susceptibility of natural soils compared to the sub-strata from which they are derived has been investigated by Le Borgne (1955, 1960). The enhancement is related to the concentration of organic matter in the soil and results from the conversion of the iron oxide from its weakly ferrimagnetic form, hæmatite (α-Fe_2O_3), to the strongly ferrimagnetic form maghæmite (γ-Fe_2O_3), already mentioned in Section 2.4.2. The conversion proceeds by reduction to magnetite and subsequent re-oxidation to maghæmite. Two possible mechanisms have been suggested. The first (Le Borgne, 1955) occurs at ordinary temperatures and is favoured by alternating periods of humidity (for reduction) and dryness (for oxidation). Too long a period of high humidity may, however, cause removal of the iron by migration (in the ferrous state) if the drainage is sufficient and then the soil will remain only weakly magnetic.

The second mechanism put forward (Le Borgne, 1960) is the cumulative effect of fire on the soil—ground clearance by burning being postulated as inherent in the methods of cultivation employed in ancient times. Although high temperatures have intervened in this case, the anomaly is due to enhancement of instantaneous susceptibility rather than thermo-remanent magnetization since the latter effect is subsequently destroyed by disarrangement as

Table 2.1. Soil susceptibilities and anomalies from unburnt features

Site	Sub-stratum	Soil susceptibilities[a] (emu/g × 10⁴)		Typical anomaly[b]
		(a) Samples not associated with archaeological features	(b) Samples from fillings of archaeological features	
Arras, Yorkshire (Iron Age barrow site)	Chalk	Plough-soil: 1·1, 1·5	Barrow ditch: 0·2, 0·15	5 gamma from barrow ditch 7 ft across, 3 ft deep. Height 2 ft
Barley, Hertfordshire (Iron Age domestic site)	Chalk	Plough-soil: 0·7, 0·8 Chalk: <0·05	Pits: 2·6, 2·1, 1·4, 1·0, 0·7	30 gamma from pit 5 ft across and 3 ft deep. Height 2·5 ft
Burrough, Leicestershire (Iron Age hill-fort)	Ferruginous limestone	Soil 6 in. below turf: 2·2, 2·4, 2·6	Pits: 7·6, 6·9, 6·8, 6·2	150 gamma from pit 3 ft across, 3 ft deep. Height 2 ft
Cox Green, Berkshire (Roman villa)	Clay	—	Ditch: 1·5 (rich black filling)	10 gamma from ditch 8 ft wide, 2–3 ft deep. Height 2 ft
Dane's Camp, Worcestershire (Iron Age hill-fort)	Limestone	Turf-layer: 7 to 11 (15 samples) Limestone: <0·05	Pits: 2 to 12 (13 samples)	100 gamma from pit 4 ft across, 5 ft deep. Height 1·5 ft (see Table 2.2)
Dorchester, Oxon. (Roman)	Gravel	Soil at 1 ft: 0·6, 0·8 Gravel: <0·05	Ditch: 1·2, 1·2, 1·1	15 gamma from ditch 10 ft wide, 3 ft deep. Height 3 ft
Enkommi, Cyprus (Bronze Age)	Limestone and clay	Soil at 6 in.: 0·7, 0·65, 0·5, 0·45	Tomb: 1·1 Well: 3·3 Road: 2·6	10 gamma from thick sun-baked road. Height 6 ft
Hod Hill, Wiltshire (Iron Age hill-fort)	Chalk	Soil 2 in. below turf: 0·6	Ditch of hut: 0·9	(4 gamma from ditch presumed 1 ft deep. Height 1 ft)
Madmarston, Oxon. (Iron Age hill-fort)	Clay	Soil 6 in. below turf: 4·0, 3·5	Pits: between 9 and 22	100 gamma from pit 6 ft across, 5 ft deep. Height 4 ft (see Table 2.2)
Water Newton, Hunts. (Roman kiln site)	Clay	Plough-soil: 1·3, 1·4, 1·6	Pit: 6·4, 5·0, 3·0	70 gamma from pit 7 ft across, 3 ft deep. Height 3 ft

[a] Susceptibilities were measured by moving the sample into the centre of the coil system described in Section 7.6.2 and observing the throw of the ballistic galvano-meter.
[b] 'Depth' refers to lowest point of feature below *old* ground surface. 'Height' refers to height of detector-bottle above *old* ground surface.

cultivation of the ground proceeds. Le Borgne has shown that burning can produce a rapid enhancement of susceptibility and to a higher degree than can be achieved with the first mechanism.

The susceptibility of artificially produced magnetite (dispersed in kaolin) and maghæmite (dispersed in sand) is of the order of 10^{-3} emu per gram for concentrations of 1 per cent (Le Borgne, 1960). However, the susceptibilities found in natural soil samples will differ widely for the same concentrations due to variations in the grain size of the magnetic particles.

2.5.2   *Pit Anomalies*

A pit creates a magnetic disturbance because its susceptibility is higher than that of the surrounding strata. If a new pit is dug and then immediately back-filled layer for layer with what was re-moved, there will be no disturbance. If the pit is left open and fills

(By kind permission of the City of Birmingham Museum and Art Gallery)

PLATE IX. Iron-age pit—Dane's Camp, Worcestershire. The soil-filling of the pit shows up clearly against the limestone into which it was dug. The bamboo marks the maximum of the magnetic anomaly and the trench was laid out so as to cut through the centre of the pit.

up by natural silting over the years, the disturbance will be moderate since it results from the small difference in susceptibility between top-soil (the silt) and sub-stratum. The disturbance is

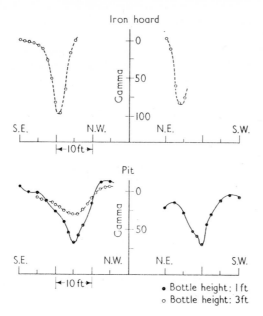

FIG. 2.10. Magnetic profiles—pit and iron hoard. The lower anomaly was due to a pit, roughly hemispherical and 7 ft across. Its top surface was 20 in. and its lower limit 4·5 ft below the present ground surface. The filling was very black soil, highly organic. Although the shape of the anomaly differs from those of the kilns in Fig. 2.9, this difference is not characteristic.

The cause of the upper anomaly was a Roman blacksmith's hoard of iron, buried about 18 in. below ground level. The magnetic gradients were too strong for the proton magnetometer to function at a lower height than 3 ft.

strong when the humus content of the pit has been artificially increased due to the addition of decaying organic matter such as waste food, dead bodies and excreta.

Pits vary in shape between cylinders and hemispheres. Their magnetization is unlikely to be uniform particularly if the filling consists of successive occupation layers. Consequently the short bar-magnet representation is a poor approximation; nor is any detailed computation of the resultant magnetic effect possible, let alone worthwhile. In practice the order of magnitude of the disturbance can be obtained by assuming the pit to be a uniformly magnetized cylinder and considering only the component of magnetization along the axis of that cylinder. This approximation has been used to calculate the average susceptibilities necessary to explain the observed anomalies from several pits, and in Table 2.2 a comparison is made with the measured susceptibilities of samples from the fillings. The order of magnitude is correct but the measured susceptibilities are consistently too low. This could arise from the inadequacy of the approximation, insufficient sampling, or because of the contribution to the anomaly of a type of magnetization additional to the susceptibility effect, e.g. viscous magnetization (see Chapter 7).

Table 2.2. Relation of pit anomalies to susceptibility of filling

Site[d]	Dimensions[b] (inches)			Anomaly (gamma)	Susceptibility necessary[c] to account for anomaly (emu/g × 10⁴)	Measured[a] susceptibilities of samples from pit filling (emu/g × 10⁴)
	a	D	h			
Madmarston	20	15	26	55	18	10
	20	15	35	30	17	
Madmarston	36	24	48	65	23	9, 19
Madmarston	24	36	27	200	33	11, 22
Madmarston	36	60	46	110	22	13
Dane's Camp	26	41	24	125	16	4·6, 4·3, 5·8, 5·4 5·4, 6·3
Dane's Camp	24	60	18	90	8·0	2·4, 1·6, 3·0, 5·0
	24	60	36	45	8·4	

[a] See note [a], Table 2.1.
[b] a = mean radius of pit, D = depth of pit below old ground surface, h = height of detector bottle above old ground surface.
[c] Calculated on 'cylinder approximation' (see text).
[d] Conditions on these two sites were exceptional and such strong anomalies should not be taken as the general rule.

In considering the likely anomaly strength it should be borne in mind that a *deep, narrow* pit is more effective than a *wide, shallow* one. Fig. 2.11 illustrates the reason. In a shallow pit the representative magnets can be regarded as side by side so that the lines of force on the axis of any magnet tend to be cancelled out by the return lines of force of adjacent magnets. In a deep pit the representative magnets are end on to each other, and at any point on the common axis the lines of force are all in the same direction.

In practice the shapes of pit anomalies are not characteristically different to kiln anomalies.

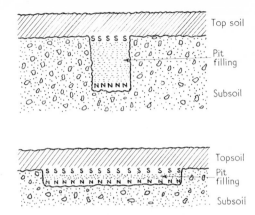

FIG. 2.11. Effect of pit shape. The anomaly from a wide, shallow pit is much smaller than from a narrow, deep one of the same volume. In the former case the induced north and south poles are close together and their magnetic fields tend to cancel.

2.6 Linear Features

While the strength of anomalies from linear features is in general much smaller than kilns and pits, there is the compensating factor of continuity. A weak disturbance over an isolated region a yard or so across can equally well arise from random variation in the top-soil as from a small pit, but a weak disturbance along a continuous line is almost certainly of archæological origin (unless it is a water main!), particularly if the line is straight, or follows a regular curve, or turns well-defined corners.

2.6.1 *Ditches*

The archæological circumstances that favour the strong magnetization of pit-fillings do not occur in ditches. Some silting of top-soil is likely but, in the main, the filling will consist of fall-in, from the rampart, of the original material excavated from the ditch. Where deliberate filling-up of the ditch has taken place before appreciable silting has occurred, the anomaly will be negligible.

Fig. 2.12 shows theoretical anomalies (computed from the data of Vacquier *et al.*, 1951) for a ditch of idealized rectangular cross-section of which the filling has a volume susceptibility of 10^{-4} emu/c.c. The anomaly from the north–south ditch is approximately twice that from an east–west ditch. In the latter case there is an appreciable *reverse* anomaly (about 20 per cent) some distance to

2*

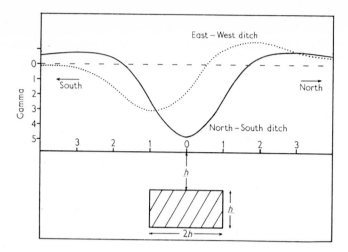

Fig. 2.12. Theoretical anomaly from ditch. Solid curve represents traverse across ditch which runs north–south. Dotted curve represents traverse across ditch which runs east–west. Idealized section of ditch is shown shaded; a volume susceptibility of 10^{-4} emu/c.c is assumed. Distance scale is in units of h.

the north of the ditch; it should not be mistaken for a separate feature such as a wall.

Figs. 2.13 and 2.14 show actual readings obtained from the right-hand ditch shown in the air photograph of Plate XI. Note the reduced strength of the anomaly for the higher bottle position (Fig. 2.13). On the other hand the left-hand ditch of Plate XI was

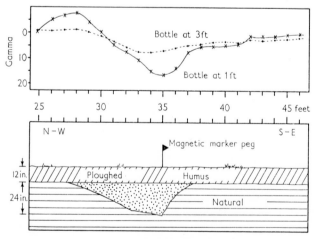

Fig. 2.13. Magnetic profile—ditch running S.W.–N.E. This ditch appears on the aerial photograph of Plate XI.

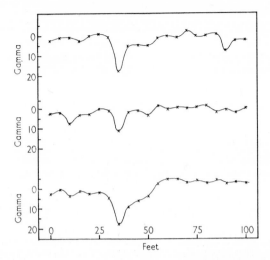

FIG. 2.14. Magnetic profiles—ditch running S.W.–N.E. Successive traverses spaced at 10 ft intervals.

not detectable; presumably in this case the magnetic contrast was insufficient and in fact, on excavation, the filling was barely distinguishable visually from the surrounding 'natural'.

The range of magnetic contrasts likely to be encountered is illustrated in Fig. 2.15. This is helpful in cases where a ditch has been sectioned at one point and it is desired to follow its course by magnetic location. A particularly successful example of this was

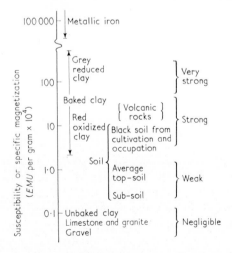

FIG. 2.15. Specific magnetization of some archæological materials.

the tracing of the inner fosse at Verulamium (Aitken, 1960); the magnetic contrast was sufficient for this to be followed despite the confusion created by isolated features, both archæological and modern, in its path. This lay through playing-fields and turned through a right-angle underneath the Corporation cricket pitch— most certainly out-of-bounds for digging! The magnetic profile is shown in Fig. 4.6.

2.6.2   Walls and Roads

Except when built of bricks or volcanic rocks, wall material is negligibly magnetic. Consequently when weakly magnetic soil is

(By kind permission of the City of Birmingham Museum and Art Gallery)

PLATE X. Wall of iron-age hut—Dane's Camp, Worcestershire. This was detected by the proton magnetometer because of pits inside the hut, and also under the wall. More pits were found by the trenches in the background—all located magnetically.

replaced by wall material a *reverse* anomaly is created. In other respects the anomaly is similar to that from a ditch and Fig. 2.12 is applicable, the susceptibility of the ditch-filling being replaced by the susceptibility of the soil which is adjacent to the wall. In practice, most walls have much smaller dimensions than ditches, and the anomaly is often undetectable unless the susceptibility of the soil is abnormally high, say 10^{-3} emu/c.c. This latter is the case for the wall of Fig. 4.5 where comparison is made with resistivity measurements.

Walls are sometimes shown up by a positive anomaly due to the accumulation of a fillet of top-soil against one edge. This also applies to roads and paved areas. In some conditions these will also show up as a reverse anomaly, but in general their thickness is too small to cause an appreciable effect. A road which has built up a great thickness of compressed, semi-baked material can create an anomaly in the normal sense.

(By kind permission of the Committee for Aerial Photography, Cambridge University)
(Ph.: J. K. St. Joseph)

PLATE XI. Aerial photography—Roman Villa at Cox Green, Berkshire. The walls of the villa appear as a light mark in the crop through reduced humidity in the soil. Two long ditches either side of the villa appear dark for the opposite reason. The ditch on the right created a magnetic disturbance but the ditch on the left did not, because the filling was too similar to the surrounding 'natural'.

2.7 Iron

The sensitivity to iron is inconveniently high; the advantage of being able to detect archæological iron is more than offset by the interfering effects of iron litter from the present intensive phase of the Iron Age. A *small* iron object produces the bar-magnet type of anomaly; since kilns and pits can also produce similar anomalies, iron is not readily distinguishable from the *shape* alone. However by rule (b) of Section 2.4.4 the *width* is equal to the depth of the cause below the detector level. Hence small iron objects lying on the

ground surface—which are almost certainly of modern origin—
can be distinguished by measuring the width of the anomaly.

Alternatively the *rate of decay* of the proton signal can be used
as an indicator of surface iron. As mentioned in Section 2.3 and
explained more fully in Section 3.2.3, a magnetic gradient of
60 gamma per foot reduces the proton signal to zero within a
second, and such 'fast decay' is easily noticed on the signal monitor
meter. The magnetic gradient along the axis of a short bar magnet
is obtained from equation (2.1) by differentiation:

$$\text{Gradient} = \frac{\mathrm{d}(\varDelta F)}{\mathrm{d}x} = \frac{\mathrm{d}}{\mathrm{d}x}\left(\frac{2M}{x^3}\right) \tag{2.2}$$
$$= \frac{-6M}{x^4} = \frac{-3(\varDelta F)}{x}$$

Thus for

$\varDelta F = 20$ gamma, fast decay will occur for x less than 1 ft

$\varDelta F = 60$ gamma, fast decay will occur for x less than 3 ft

$\varDelta F = 200$ gamma, fast decay will occur for x less than 10 ft

etc.

Although for *small* anomalies 'fast decay' is indicative of surface
iron, for *large* ones it can equally well result from a kiln or pit, or
iron lying below the surface.

The discussion above applies to small iron objects on the surface,
e.g. nails, horseshoes, marking-out skewers. Extended ironwork
such as chicken-netting, bedstead frames, etc. is more easily
recognizable; irregular shape and magnetization produce an
irregular anomaly sometimes in the reverse direction, and this is
almost always sufficient to produce 'fast decay'. In fact the decay
is usually too rapid for the frequency measurement to be made,
and an obviously spurious count is indicated.

A useful rule of thumb is that the *maximum* specific magnetization to be expected in scrap cast iron is about 10 emu/g. Assuming
it behaves as a short bar magnet (so that the inverse cube law of
equation (2.1) is applicable), an anomaly of 1 gamma can be
produced by:

1 gram (0·002 lb) of iron at a distance not exceeding 1 metre

or, 125 gram (0·3 lb) of iron at a distance not exceeding 5 metres

or, 1 kilogram (2·2 lb) of iron at a distance not exceeding 10 metres

Actual iron anomalies differ greatly from this owing to varying
susceptibilities and coercive forces; also, if the magnetization is

remanent, the piece of iron may be lying at such an angle that change in total field strength is negligible (see Fig. 2.5). On the other hand, a small nail, close to the detector, in a wooden marking-out peg, can sometimes produce as strong an anomaly as a pottery kiln; the *width* of the disturbance (or 'fast decay') quickly identifies it, but it may mask some genuine archæological feature.

Finally, the most likely source of iron interference of all is in the clothing of the bottle operator. Zip fasteners, hairpins, watches, keys, penknives and bootnails can all cause trouble, but by no means consistently. The instrument itself must be kept at a distance greater than 20 ft.

2.8 Survey Logistics

2.8.1 *Size of Measurement Mesh*

Closely spaced measurements are necessary for three reasons:

(*i*) Many 'magnetic features' are only a yard across, and the magnetic disturbance does not spread much beyond.

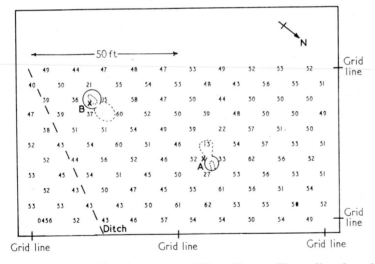

FIG. 2.16. Sample readings from survey at Water Newton. The readings from the last two meters only are recorded unless any change occurs in the others. One unit equals 1 gamma. The bottle height was 3 ft. The features subsequently found by excavation were two kilns (marked A and B) and a ditch. The outlines of the kilns and stokeholes are shown. The crosses indicate the maximum of the anomaly found by closer investigation (see Fig. 2.9).

The readings shown cover two 'squares', an area 50 ft by 100 ft. In this survey the readings were taken on a triangular mesh, 50 readings per square. This saved time over the usual square mesh which involves 100 readings per square.

(*ii*) The *absolute value* of the magnetic intensity may vary over the site due to geological causes (e.g. slowly changing depth of top-soil); archæological effects are distinguishable by a sharp *change* of intensity over a distance comparable with the expected width (or depth) of the feature.

(*iii*) To obtain sufficiently precise localization of the feature for economy in excavation.

(*iv*) Even if the survey is for large features a close mesh immediately discriminates against small iron objects on the surface since only one measurement will be affected in the latter case.

For small near-surface features a mesh size of 1 ft is worthwhile but a reasonable compromise between time and efficiency is a mesh of 5 ft with interpolation where disturbances are detected. Excluding interpolation, a well organized team can cover an acre in 4 hours.

The area is first marked out with stout pegs so as to form a grid of 50-ft squares. Each square is covered in turn by a net stretched between the four corner pegs; the mesh size of the net is 10 ft and the middle of each 10-ft length is marked with a coloured tag so that the bottle operator can judge the additional positions needed for the 5 ft mesh by eye. On a 5 ft mesh there are 100 new positions per 50-ft square, approximately 1800 per acre.

Ordinary string is no use for constructing the net owing to shrinkage in wet weather. *Varnished glass tying cord** ($\frac{1}{8}$ in. diameter) is used instead. The reeling-out of the net is probably the most skilled operation in magnetic surveying!

A sample of the readings recorded during a survey is shown in Fig. 2.16.

2.8.2 *Choice of Bottle Height*

With decreasing height, the anomaly strength increases, but random variations due to surface irregularities and surface iron are relatively greater. Where the top-soil thickness is a foot or more there is not much gain in sensitivity by decreasing the bottle height from 2 ft to 1 ft, but the disturbance from a nail on the surface will be increased by a factor of eight. On the other hand, if the bottle height is made too great, the small anomalies may be masked by irregular changes due to passing cars, and the transient variations in the earth's field (see Section 2.2.4).

---

* It is most important that the cord is varnished, otherwise abrasion is rapid. Suitable cord is manufactured by Jones, Stroud & Co., Canal St., Long Eaton, Nottingham, England.

Thus the optimum height varies with local conditions. In general, the deeper the feature the higher the bottle, but the height should never exceed the mesh-spacing in use.

2.8.3 *Correcting for the Transient Variation*

When looking for small anomalies (10 gamma or less) on 'magnetic storm' days it is necessary to use a second bottle in a fixed position. The instrument is switched to this after every tenth measurement and appropriate corrections made. It is sufficient to relate the readings of each 50 ft square to an individual arbitrary level since it is only small-scale changes that are archæologically significant.

2.8.4 *Site Hazards*

(*i*) *Igneous Geology.* The thermo-remanent magnetism of some igneous (and metamorphic) rocks is strong enough to mask the archæological anomalies. This applies particularly to recent volcanics of the tertiary period and later. The interference from granites and older volcanics may be weak enough to permit surveying.

(*ii*) *Extraneous Iron.* It can be taken for granted that on any site in the vicinity of present habitation there will be too much iron litter to make surveying worthwhile. In addition there is the possibility of water pipes and gas mains. In the open country corrugated iron and wire fences are the most frequent hazards; as a general rule the disturbance from a wire fence is objectionable up to a distance of 30 ft.

(*iii*) *D.C. Electric Trains.* The magnetic effects from the forward and return currents should cancel out, but because very large currents are involved (3000 amps or so) a small percentage of earth leakage can cause sufficient unbalance to produce interfering effects up to 10 miles from the line. The effect consists of sharp changes in the field strength as trains start and stop *anywhere along that line.*

(*iv*) *A.C. Electrical Power.* This does not affect the average field strength, but electromagnetic pick-up by the bottle-coil may drown the proton signal and cause the count to be inaccurate. Power cables are not usually troublesome except on the ground directly below them; transformer sub-stations are much more serious.

(*v*) *Trees and Undergrowth.* The practical difficulty of moving the cable and the net rules out sites covered in trees and bushes; long grass, thistles, and rock débris can be very tedious too.

(*vi*) *General*. Irregular ground surfaces, unfilled trenches or spoil heaps are all liable to produce minor disturbances. Filled-in trenches from previous excavations may produce a weak anomaly merely because the ground is disturbed; in addition iron marking-out skewers are likely.

2.9   The Differential Magnetometer

The criterion for distinguishing archæological from geological features is a sharp change over a distance of a few feet. Hence a *differential* magnetometer, which measures the *difference* in the magnetic intensity experienced by two bottles fixed at either end of a 5-ft rod, will respond only to archæological features. At the same time it eliminates large-scale interference effects due to the transient variations, automobiles, trains and electric trains.

It seems likely that the differential magnetometer will replace the absolute form for archæological surveying. A simple and cheap version of this instrument (the 'Bleeper'), sufficiently sensitive for detecting strong and medium anomalies (a difference of 10 gamma and upwards) is described in Section 3.5. In operation (see Plate XV) the rod carrying the two bottles can be held vertically since wherever there is a magnetic gradient in the horizontal direction there is also one in the vertical direction; this simplifies interpretation. When there is no gradient, the 'bleeper' loudspeaker emits a steady note. If the magnetic intensities between the two bottle positions differ, the note fluctuates at the *beat frequency* (i.e. the difference between the individual frequencies) of the two proton signals. If the 'listening time' is $2\frac{1}{2}$ seconds:

1 beat corresponds to a difference of more than 10 gamma
2 beats correspond to a difference of more than 20 gamma
etc.

Human counting ability limits the *maximum* measurable difference to 100 gamma. This is not a serious restriction on most sites; it could be overcome by electrical counting or the use of resonant reeds. Reduction of the *minimum* measurable difference much below 5 gamma requires electrical circuitry of a complexity comparable with that of the absolute magnetometer. An alternative possibility is the use of a differential *flux-gate* magnetometer.

The most serious disadvantage of the simple 'Bleeper' is that it does not determine whether the anomaly is positive or negative, i.e. it cannot tell walls from ditches. This additional information could be obtained by the use of a small annulling magnetic bias field of known polarity.

References

Aitken, M. J., 1959: Magnetic prospecting—An interim assessment. *Antiquity*, **33**, 205–207

Aitken, M. J., 1960: The magnetic survey. Appendix to S. S. Frere: Excavations at Verulamium 1959, 5th Interim Report. *Antiquaries Journal*, **40**, 21–24

Haigh, G., 1958: The process of magnetization by chemical change. *Phil. Mag.*, **3**, 267

Le Borgne, E., 1955: Susceptibilité magnétique anormale du sol superficiel. *Ann. Géophys.*, **11**, 399–419

Le Borgne, E., 1960: Influence du feu sur les propriétés magnétiques du sol. *Ann. Géophys.*, **16**, 159–195

Smellie, D. W., 1956: Elementary approximations in aeromagnetic interpretation. *Geophysics*, **21**, 1021–1039

Vacquier, V., Steenland, N. C., Henderson, R. G. and Zietz, I., 1951: Interpretation of aeromagnetic maps. *Geol. Soc. Amer. Memoir*, No. 47

CHAPTER 3

THE PROTON MAGNETOMETER

3.1 Introduction

The magnetic location technique, described in the last chapter, is a practical proposition only if the detecting instrument, in addition to being sufficiently sensitive, is speedy and simple to operate. The *proton magnetometer* meets these requirements. A preliminary description of the instrument has been given in Section 2.3. However, as the simplicity of operation is achieved by electrical circuits that are somewhat complex, and as the physical phenomenon involved is of comparatively recent discovery, the present chapter is devoted to a fuller treatment. *Non-scientists are advised to omit it.*

3.2 Free Precession

The *free precession* of protons in the earth's magnetic field was first observed experimentally in 1953 (Packard and Varian, 1954), the effect having been predicted in 1946 (Bloch, 1946). It depends on the same nuclear properties as *nuclear magnetic resonance* ('NMR'), widely used for the measurement of strong magnetic fields and the investigation of chemical structure, but, as the word 'free' implies, no resonance is involved.

Nuclear magnetic resonance experiments are analogous to the measurement of the time of swing of a pendulum by applying to it a periodic force and finding at what applied frequency the swings are the biggest, whereas free precession corresponds to the simpler method of giving the pendulum an initial displacement from the vertical and timing a given number of swings with a stop-watch.

Thus, in nuclear magnetic resonance measurements, an alternating magnetic field is *applied* to the sample of nuclei, and, if the frequency is correct, the nuclei precess in *resonance*. With free precession, there is no *applied* frequency, and the signal observed is simply the e.m.f. generated in a coil by the rotating magnetic moment formed by a large number of nuclei precessing in phase.

Consider the *gyration* of a spinning top (see Fig. 3.1). The gravitational force *mg* tends to twist the axis of the top but, because the top has an angular momentum about its own axis, the resulting motion is in a direction perpendicular both to the axis of the top and to the gravitational force mg; one complete gyration of the top is shown by the dotted circle. The frequency of gyration, f, is given by the relation:

$$2\pi f = \frac{mgh \sin \theta}{p \sin \theta}$$

$$\text{i.e.} \quad f = \frac{mgh}{2\pi p}$$

In the absence of frictional effects the angle, θ, between the vertical and the axis of the top would remain constant indefinitely.

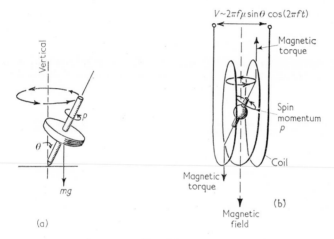

FIG. 3.1

(a) Spinning top under the influence of gravity.
(b) Proton under the influence of a magnetic field.
    The voltage induced in the coil has the same *frequency* as the proton gyrations irrespective of the proton orientation. The orientation affects only the *amplitude* of the voltage.

Resulting from the property called 'intrinsic spin' the proton has an angular momentum (p) and a magnetic moment (μ) both along the same axis. In a magnetic field F (see Fig. 3.1b) there is a couple $\mu F \sin \theta$ tending to align the proton in the same direction as F but because of its spin momentum it gyrates, like the top. In this case the frequency is given by the relation

$$f = \frac{\mu F}{2\pi p} \tag{3.1}$$

which, as before, is independent of the angle θ. Since μ and p are strictly invariant, this frequency depends only on F. For the proton the ratio (μ/p) is $26753 \cdot 0$ sec^{-1} oersted^{-1} so that

$$f = 4257 \cdot 6 \times F \text{ cycles per sec} \qquad (3 \cdot 2)$$

Since F varies between $0 \cdot 25$ and $0 \cdot 7$ oersted at different parts of the earth's surface, the frequency is always within the audio range.

Free precession occurs with many other nuclei besides the proton. However, for ease and accuracy of measurement as high a frequency as possible is desirable, and the ratio (μ/p), the *magnetogyric ratio*, is highest for the proton. Besides this, protons are present in water as the nuclei of hydrogen atoms so that water forms a convenient and readily available sample.

3.2.1   *Detection*

If a coil is placed with its axis roughly perpendicular to the magnetic field, the amplitude of the e.m.f. generated in it is proportional to $f\mu \sin \theta$. The *amplitude* is of interest only because it must be large enough for an accurate measurement of the *frequency*.

The signal produced by a single proton is of course infinitesimal, and for detection to be feasible a large number of protons must precess together, *in phase*. This is achieved by subjecting the sample to a strong *polarizing* field before each measurement. Fig. 3.2

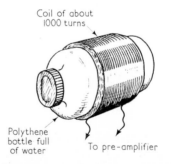

Coil of about
1000 turns

Polythene
bottle full
of water

To pre-amplifier

Fɪɢ. 3.2. Detector bottle for proton magnetometer.

shows a suitable experimental arrangement. The water sample of 200 c.c is contained in a polythene bottle around which is wound a coil of 1000 turns. This coil serves both for detection and polarization, by means of suitable switching relays (see Section 3.5.1). During polarization a steady current of about 1 amp is passed through the coil, creating a magnetic field of several hundred oersteds along the axis. This tends to align the protons but, because of thermal agitation, at equilibrium the fractional alignment is only $(\mu F/kT)$, where k is Boltzmann's constant and T is the absolute temperature. At normal temperatures $(T \approx 290°\mathrm{K})$ and for $F = 200$ oersteds, this fraction is about 10^{-7}. In 1 c.c of water there are approximately 7×10^{22} protons so that since the value of μ is $1\cdot4 \times 10^{-23}$ emu, the resulting magnetic moment per c.c is equal to $(10^{-7} \times 7 \times 10^{22} \times 1\cdot4 \times 10^{-23}) \approx 10^{-7}$ gauss.

When the polarizing current is shut off, this induced magnetization gyrates at a frequency of about 2000 c/s (assuming $F \approx 0\cdot5$ oersted), thereby inducing a voltage in the coil (diameter 5 cm) given by

$$
\begin{aligned}
V &= (2\pi \times 2000) \times (4\pi \times 10^{-7}) \times (\pi \times 2\cdot5^2 \times 1000) \\
&\qquad \sin(2\pi \times 2000)t \text{ emu} \\
&= 3 \sin(2\pi \times 2000)t \text{ microvolts.}
\end{aligned}
$$

This will be detectable, after amplification, as long as it is large compared to the random electrical noise. Taking the resistance of the coil to be 10 ohms and the noise factor of the input pre-amplifier to be 10 (20 decibels), the theoretical coil noise amounts to about $0\cdot02$ microvolts for an amplifier bandwidth of 20 c/s. In practice a signal-to-noise ratio of 50:1 is obtainable.

3.2.2 *Signal Decay*

Interfering magnetic fields from neighbouring nuclei perturb the proton gyrations, causing the protons to get out of step (i.e. lose phase coherence) so that the resultant magnetic moment slowly decreases to zero; in addition, the excess of protons having $\theta \approx 90°$ with respect to the earth's field, F, changes gradually to an excess for $\theta = 0$. The decay of the signal is exponential, and the time taken for the amplitude to decrease by a factor of $2\cdot7$ is termed the *relaxation time*. For distilled water, the relaxation time is about 3 sec. Consequently, the signal is only big enough for accurate frequency determination for a few seconds after each polarizing period.

The relaxation time is also relevant to the duration of the polarizing period. The equilibrium fractional alignment of $(\mu F/kT)$ is reached only for an indefinitely long polarization; if the duration is equal to the relaxation time, the fractional alignment is two-thirds of the equilibrium value. Strictly one should distinguish between the *longitudinal* (or *spin–lattice*) *relaxation time*, T_1, applicable to the polarizing process, and the *transverse* (or *spin–spin*) *relaxation time*, T_2, applicable to the decay of the gyrating magnetic moment. Although for water and many other liquids the two are approximately equal, for crystalline solids T_2 is very much shorter than T_1.

The presence of dissolved paramagnetic impurities reduces the relaxation time. Thus the presence in water of a ferric salt, to a concentration of a 0·001 molar solution, reduces T_1 to 0·1 sec; for cupric salts the same reduction occurs at ten times this concentration. To achieve the full value for water, any dissolved oxygen must be removed, since *free* oxygen is paramagnetic. In pure water and organic liquids, the interfering fields arise solely from neighbouring protons since both the oxygen nucleus and the carbon nucleus have zero magnetic moment; the atomic magnetic moment of free oxygen disappears when it combines chemically.

In general, liquids of low viscosity have long relaxation times. In these the rapid molecular diffusion smooths out the interfering magnetic fields from neighbouring nuclei. As the temperature of a liquid is lowered towards freezing point, T_2 decreases, and on solidification it becomes very short indeed. The smoothing-out effect is then lost, and the internal fields cause a spread in the gyration frequencies of individual protons. The bigger this spread, the quicker is the loss of phase coherence.

3.2.3 *Effect of External Field Gradient*

Loss of phase coherence (or 'getting out-of-step') can also occur if the *external* field is different for different parts of the sample. A uniform gradient such that the overall difference is 10 gamma reduces the signal to zero in just over one second. This corresponds to a gradient of about 60 gamma per ft; this is not exceptional in the proximity of buildings. *Inside* a building the gradients are intolerably high.

3.3 Frequency Measurement

Normal methods of frequency measurement are not applicable because the proton signal dies away within a few seconds even in a uniform magnetic field. In a non-uniform field the decay is quicker still, and the less time required for measurement, the higher the gradient that can be tolerated. In addition, it is necessary to measure the frequency to within a fraction of a cycle, for a change in field strength of 1 gamma in a total field of 50 000 gamma corresponds to a frequency change of only 0·04 c/s.

The problem has been tackled in two ways. The first way, developed by Varian Associates,* utilizes the fast response of resonant reeds, and is essentially an extension of beat-frequency methods; the sensitivity is limited to 10 gamma. The second approach, developed in Britain at the Signals Research and Development Establishment (Waters and Francis, 1958; Bradshaw, 1957), involves electrical counting of the cycles of the proton signal; a sensitivity of 1 gamma is easily obtainable. Both systems

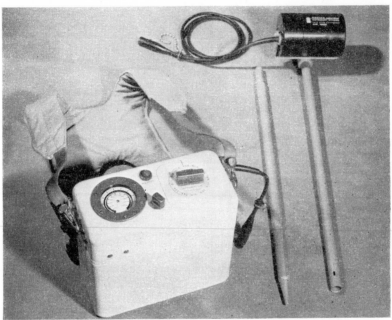

(*By kind permission of Varian Associates*)

PLATE XII. The proton magnetometer—Varian Associates, Model M-49.
Left: Electronic package with shoulder strap.
Right: Detector bottle with monopod.

can be fully transistorized. The instrument referred to in the previous chapter is of the latter type†; besides its greater sensitivity, its ability to function in sharper magnetic gradients makes it the better one for archæological work.

3.3.1 *The Resonant Reed Technique*

Fig. 3.3 shows a simplified block diagram. The reference frequency is provided by mixing the outputs of two crystal-controlled

* Varian Associates, Palo Alto, California. (See Plate XII.)

† Now manufactured commercially by the Littlemore Scientific Engineering Co., Littlemore, Oxford, England. (See Plate XIII.)

(By kind permission of Littlemore Scientific Engineering Co., Oxford)
(Ph.: Thomas-Photos, Oxford)
PLATE XIII. The proton magnetometer—'The Elsec'.

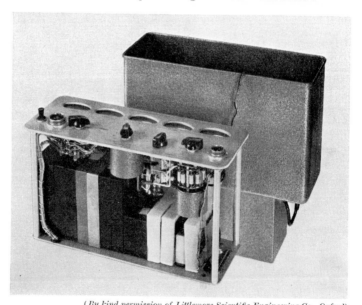

(By kind permission of Littlemore Scientific Engineering Co., Oxford)
(Ph.: Thomas-Photos, Oxford)
PLATE XIV. The proton magnetometer—'The Elsec'. All the transistor circuits
are contained in plug-in units.

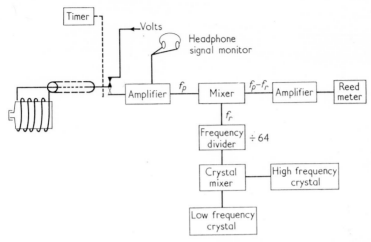

FIG. 3.3. The resonant reed technique. The reference frequency, f_r, obtained by frequency division from two crystal oscillators can be switched to be within 120 c/s of the proton signal frequency, f_p. The resultant beat frequency $(f_p - f_r)$ is indicated on the resonant reed meter.

oscillators and then dividing the sum frequency by means of a six-stage binary chain. By switching different crystals into the oscillator units, the resultant frequency (f_r) can be adjusted so that it is within 120 c/s of the proton signal frequency (f_p). The difference frequency ($f_p - f_r$) between the proton signal and the reference signal is then amplified, and applied to the resonant reed meter. This carries 53 reeds each of which resonates at a particular frequency; these frequencies are equally spaced over a range of 42 c/s. Thus by reading the setting of the crystal selector switches and noting which reed is resonating, the frequency of the proton signal can be deduced. In practice the switches and the reeds are calibrated directly in gamma.

3.3.2 The Cycle-Counting Technique

Essentially this consists of measuring the number of cycles of a 100 kc crystal-controlled oscillator that occur during the time taken for the proton signal to complete a fixed number of cycles. A convenient number in practice is 1024. The measurement is thus complete in $\frac{1}{2}$ sec for a total field of 50 000 gamma, and in 1 sec for a field as low as 25 000 gamma.

After selective amplification to several volts the sinusoidal signal of decaying amplitude is shaped to a constant amplitude square wave of identical frequency (see Fig. 3.4b). This square wave is frequency divided by a ten-stage binary chain, so that,

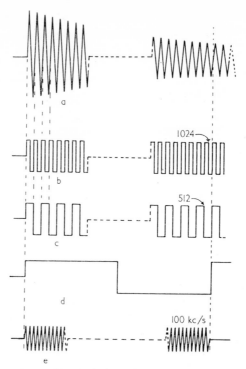

FIG. 3.4. The cycle-counting technique. Waveforms. (a) Proton signal from amplifier, $f \approx 2000$ c/s. (b) Proton signal after squaring, $f \approx 2000$ c/s. (c) After frequency division by one binary stage, $f \approx 1000$ c/s. (d) After frequency division by ten binary stages, $f \approx 2$ c/s. (e) Gated output of 100 kc oscillator.

since $2^{10} = 1024$, the frequency after the tenth stage is approximately 2 c/s (see Fig. 3.4d). This is applied, via a locking unit, to a gate such that the first positive-going edge entering the locking unit opens the gate and the next closes it, the gate then remaining closed until the unit is reset. When the gate is open the output of the 100 kc crystal-controlled oscillator is fed to a decade chain (see Fig. 3.5). The operation of each decade unit is such that one pulse appears at the output for every ten that enter at the input, and if the number entering is not a multiple of ten the number remaining after division by ten is indicated on the corresponding digital meter. Thus the 5-digit number indicated by these five meters equals the number of 100 kc oscillator pulses that get through the gate. Since the gate remains open for 1024 proton gyrations the decade count is given by

$$n = 100\,000 \times \frac{1024}{f} \qquad (3.3)$$

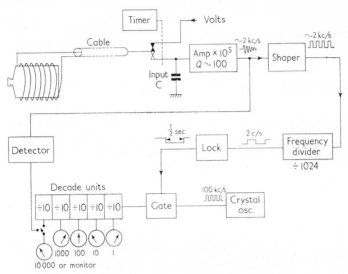

F<small>IG</small>. 3.5. Cycle-counting technique: block diagram. The decade meters record the number of 100 kc oscillator pulses that pass through the gate while it is held open for the duration of 1024 proton pulses. A locking unit ('lock') ensures the gate subsequently remains closed until about 0·1 sec after another polarization has been completed.

so from equation (3.2)

$$F = \frac{24,050}{n} \text{ oersted} \qquad (3.4)$$

Thus for $F \approx 0.5$ oersted, a *decrease* of n by 1 unit corresponds to an *increase* of F by 1 gamma (0·00001 oersted), a sensitivity of 1 part in 50000. The crucial point in maintaining this is the time-accuracy of the base-line crossings of the proton signal (Fig. 3.4a) that correspond to opening and closing of the gate. The error must be less than 10 μsec, i.e. $\frac{1}{50}$ of a proton cycle; this requires that the signal-to-noise ratio is better than 10 to 1 at the end of the measuring period.

The sensitivity can be increased, say to 1 part in 100000, by counting off 2048 proton pulses instead of 1024. Use of a 1 megacycle oscillator would, in principle, improve this to 1 part in 10^6 but, in practice, the necessary signal-to-noise ratio might be difficult to attain.

The *absolute* accuracy of the instrument depends on the calibration of the crystal-controlled oscillator. A good oscillator will remain constant to 1 part in 100000, over the temperature range 10°C to 40°C.

3.4 Differential Measurements

In locating archæological features, magnetic *gradient* is more significant than the absolute intensity. Although strong gradients are shown up by a faster decay of the proton signal (see Section 3.2.3) this method is insufficiently sensitive for many archæological features and also, it favours the detection of unwanted surface iron. These difficulties are avoided by measuring the *difference* in the magnetic intensities experienced by two detecting bottles separated by a few feet, i.e. the average gradient over a distance comparable with the depth or width of the archæological feature, rather than the gradient at a point. Of course this is effectively what is done during interpretation when making absolute measurements but it is more convenient to use an instrument which indicates the difference directly.

Ideally one requires two proton magnetometers which feed into a common decade chain but in opposite senses, i.e. the count from one is automatically subtracted from that from the other, the meters indicating the difference. The increased complexity is considerable, particularly if the two are to operate simultaneously; this latter is desirable in order to eliminate interference from d.c. power-lines and passing automobiles, etc.

3.4.1 *The 'Beat Gradiometer'*

A simpler, though less precise method, is to add together the proton signals from the two bottles before amplification and dispense with the binary and decade chains. The bottles are fed by a common polarizing current so that at its cessation, the initial proton signals are in phase. If the two bottles are in the same field strength then the sum of the two signals has twice the individual amplitudes and decays away to zero in the usual way. If the bottles experience different fields, then the frequencies are different and although the initial resultant amplitude is the same as before, subsequently the amplitude fluctuates as the two signals successively get in and out of phase. This is the well-known phenomenon of *beats*. The 'beat frequency' is the frequency difference between the two component signals.

The limit of sensitivity is set by the minimum beat frequency that can be detected. A difference of 1 gamma corresponds to a frequency of only 0·04 c/s; this will certainly go undetected since the signal decays in a few seconds anyway. However, a difference of 5 gamma produces a beat frequency of 0·2 c/s, causing the resultant amplitude of the two signals to reach its first zero in

2·5 sec; this is distinguishable from the case of equal fields since in the latter case the proton signal still retains one-third of its initial amplitude at that time.

The rate of decay can be timed electrically but a limit is set to the accuracy obtainable by fluctuations in the relative initial sizes of the two proton signals and in their decay-rates. For archæological work an accurate measurement is not important, and observation of the decay rate, by eye or ear, can easily detect differences corresponding to 10 gamma, and with practice to 5 gamma. This is sensitive enough for many types of archæological feature. A suitable instrument, simple and inexpensive,* has been developed by the Archæological Research Laboratory at Oxford. Its construction is within the competence of the average radio engineer, and in the description that follows, stress is laid upon those parts of the circuits unlikely to be encountered normally.

3.5   The 'Bleeper'

Fig. 3.6 shows the block diagram of the instrument. The two bottle-coils are connected in series so that the polarizing current is broken by a single relay contact; besides ensuring that the two proton signals have the same phase, the series arrangement accomplishes the addition of the two signals before the pre-amplifier, thus avoiding the need for any special mixing circuit later on.

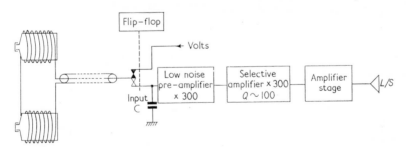

FIG. 3.6. Beat gradiometer—the 'Bleeper'. The 2 kc note heard from the loudspeaker fluctuates at the beat frequency of the two proton signals. A beat frequency of 1 c/s corresponds to a magnetic field difference of 25 gamma.

The timing flip-flop automatically controls the relay system so that polarizing periods alternate with 'listening' periods as long as the instrument is switched-on. Normally the duration of each period is 2·5 sec, giving a minimum detectable magnetic field

* Components cost roughly £50.

difference of 5 gamma. A longer listening period gives greater sensitivity (as long as the relaxation time of the liquid is not greatly exceeded) while a longer polarizing time gives a stronger signal. The two bottles are fixed at either end of a rod 5 ft long (see Plate XV); this rod is held vertical by the operator and a

(*Ph.*: M. J. Aitken)

PLATE XV. Differential proton magnetometer—the 'Bleeper'.

second rod, 6 in. or 1 ft in length, determines the height of the lower bottle above turf level. In the absence of magnetic distur-bance the 2000 c/s note from the loudspeaker is steady throughout each listening period. Over a weak disturbance the note ceases before the listening period is complete; over a strong one beats (or 'bleeps') are heard, the number of beats within the listening period indicating the strength of the disturbance and this increases to a maximum when the centre of the disturbance is reached.

The average power consumption (including the polarizing cur-rent) is less than $\frac{1}{2}$ amp so that a set of 8 amp-hour miniature 12-V accumulators lasts for two days' operation without recharging (which in any case can be done in a series–parallel arrangement from an automobile accumulator).

3.5.1   *Input Relay Circuits*

The relay circuits perform the following functions:

(*i*) *During the polarizing period* the 12-V supply is connected to the coaxial cable leading to the two bottles. The resistance of the two bottles, which are in series, plus that of 100 ft of coaxial cable amounts to 17 ohms, so that the current flowing is 0·7 amp.

(*ii*) *At the conclusion of the polarizing period*, the polarizing current must be broken sharply; the final collapse of the current must occur in a time short compared to a millisecond, otherwise the alignment of the protons is destroyed. Standard relay contacts fulfil this condition adequately as long as they do not feed an inductive load other than the bottle-coils.

(*iii*) *To avoid overloading*, the input to the pre-amplifier must be earthed during the break of the polarizing current, and before it is connected to the bottle-coils, any oscillations in the latter set off by the break must be damped out.

(*iv*) *During the 'listening' period*, the bottle-coils must form a tuned circuit with the input tuning condenser; the input impedance of the pre-amplifier must not load down this tuned circuit too heavily. A Q-factor of 20 is adequate and easily obtainable; a higher Q-factor is undesirable, firstly because it would involve altering the value of the tuning condenser for small changes of magnetic intensity, and secondly because the high currents flowing in the coil of a high Q circuit would interact with the gyrating protons and reduce the effective relaxation time.

Because of the high overall gain of the system great care must be taken to avoid multiple earthing points in the input circuits and also capacitative pick-up.

Fig. 3.7 shows a suitable circuit. The timing flip-flop alternately energizes and de-energizes RL 1 corresponding to listening and polarizing periods respectively; each period is normally 2·5 sec but this can be altered if desired by adjustment of the flip-flop time constants. Alternatively the operation could be controlled manually, RL 1 being replaced by a two-pole switch.

The sequence of events is as follows:

(*i*) *During the polarizing period*, RL 1 is de-energized, and both contacts are closed. Contact 1b feeds power to RL 2, which closes 2a and 2c but opens 2b. Power reaches the bottle-coils via contacts 1a and 2a.

(*ii*) *At the conclusion of the polarizing period*, RL 1 is energized and 1a opens thus breaking the bottle-coil current; although sparking occurs (because of the inductive load of the bottle),

3+

standard heavy-duty contacts will stand up to this for a long time. It is important that 1b does not open while this spark across 1a persists. The contacts should be bent so that 1a opens just in advance of 1b.

(*iii*) *Pre-amplifier overloading* is avoided because the condenser–resistance circuit in parallel with RL 2 holds it energized for a further 20 milliseconds. During this delay period any unwanted oscillations in the bottle-coils are damped by the 10 kΩ resistor which is effectively across the cable, and the pre-amplifier input is still earthed via contact 2c.

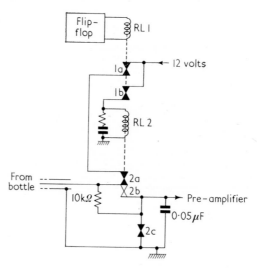

Fig. 3.7. Input relay circuit. Black contacts closed during polarizing period. White contacts closed during listening period.

(*iv*) *During the listening period*, the bottle-coil cable is connected across the tuning condenser via contact 2b. At the same time contact 2a isolates the input from capacitative pick-up across contacts 1a; this comes from the supply voltage, which since it feeds the later amplifying stages, carries a small ripple at the signal frequency.

Since the combined bottle-coil inductance is 0·12 henry, the pre-amplifier input impedance must be between 50 kΩ and 100 kΩ in order to obtain a Q-factor of 20.

3.5.2 Amplifying Circuits

The transistor circuits used follow standard audio practice and will not be described in detail. The high input impedance of the pre-amplifier can be obtained with an emitter–follower stage, and the use of high-stability components and low-noise transistors (noise figure should be 5 dB or less) in the first two stages meets noise requirements. It is also advantageous to keep down the low frequency response of all stages prior to the amplifier tuned circuit.

In order to reduce noise and to avoid interference, the bandwidth of the amplifier should not exceed 20 c/s. A suitable tuned circuit consists of a ferroxcube coil wound with 2000 turns of 36 S.W.G. in parallel with a fixed 2000 pF capacitor and a 500 pF trimming capacitor. The latter is necessary since a bandwidth of 20 c/s implies a range of magnetic intensity coverage of only 500 gamma; such a variation can easily be exceeded between different sites. The tuned circuit is matched to the transistors by means of a 1:60 tapping on the coil, and it is connected to the collector of the first-stage transistor.

The amplifier feeding the loudspeaker should be operated under 'Class C' conditions such that the signal amplitude necessary to produce saturation intensity in the loudspeaker is only slightly greater than the threshold signal necessary to produce any note at all. In this way a note of nearly constant intensity is heard as long as the proton signal amplitude is above threshold. This level is adjusted to be slightly lower than the signal amplitude remaining at the end of the listening period, when the bottles are in equal magnetic fields. Consequently, a weak magnetic disturbance, although insufficient to produce 'bleeps', is easily detectable because of the complete cessation of the note before the end of the listening period, which is indicated by a sharp 'bleep' due to pick-up from the switch-on of the polarizing current by relay contacts RL 1a.

3.6 The Detector Bottle

The liquid is contained in a plastic bottle of capacity 200 c.c and diameter 1·85 in. The coil is pile-wound (layer winding is not necessary) over a 2-in. length of the bottle and consists of approximately 1250 turns of 22 S.W.G. single enamel copper. The number of turns is adjusted to give an inductance of 0·062 henry and the resulting resistance is about 7 ohms. The coil is terminated in an aluminium socket (brass is unsuitable because of ferromagnetic impurities) and the whole assembly is encapsulated in a casting resin (e.g. 'Marco' resin type S.B. 28C made by Scott Bader). Connections to the bottle are made with coaxial cable (Uniradio 70), and again, the plugs must be of aluminium. The coils are connected in opposition so that any airborne electromagnetic pick-up (e.g. radio transmissions) cancel out.

The details of bottle construction are not critical *except*, firstly the avoidance of even slightly magnetic materials, and secondly the exclusion of all traces of moisture from the coil itself (deterioration of the proton signal from this cause may occur long before any effect on the Q-factor of the coil is noticeable).

3.6.1 *Choice of Liquid*

The basic requirements for the filling liquid are:

(i) That the amplitude of the proton signal is large enough to give a good signal-to-noise ratio (the noise arises from the input stages of the pre-amplifier so that increased amplification cannot compensate for a poor initial signal-to-noise ratio). For a given polarizing current the amplitude is proportional to the number of protons per c.c.

(ii) That the relaxation time, T, is suitable. If T is too short the signal dies away before any beats are heard. If T is too long, the polarizing time has to be increased in order to obtain sufficient amplitude, and this will slow down the survey. On the other hand the longer the relaxation time, the greater the sensitivity.

Although water is widely used for proton magnetometers it has two serious disadvantages:

(i) It freezes in cold weather; this will prevent operation temporarily because the relaxation time of ice is very short (as for any other solid—the averaging out effect of low viscosity being entirely lost) but also, the expansion of ice as the temperature falls may burst the bottle.

(ii) Any slight leakage of water onto the coil causes deterioration of the signal.

Suitable alternatives to water are methyl alcohol, hexane and heptane.

To achieve the maximum relaxation time the liquid must be pure and free from dissolved oxygen; distillation in an atmosphere of nitrogen immediately prior to filling achieves both of these conditions. On the other hand results can in fact be obtained simply by using ordinary distilled water or laboratory alcohol. The author has obtained a proton signal, though short, from a coil immersed directly in domestic paraffin.

References

Bloch, F., 1946: Nuclear induction. *Phys. Rev.*, **70**, 461
Bradshaw, C. G., 1957: A versatile 100 Kc/s transistor counter chronometer for frequency measurement. *S.R.D.E. Report* No. 1106

Packard, M. and Varian, R., 1954: Free nuclear induction in the earth's magnetic field. *Phys. Rev.*, **93**, 941

Waters, G. S. and Francis, P. D., 1958: A nuclear magnetometer. *J. sci. Instrum.*, **35**, 88–93

CHAPTER 4

RESISTIVITY SURVEYING

4.1 Introduction

Magnetic anomalies are present all the time and the function of the magnetometer is solely that of detector. In resistivity surveying, an electrical voltage is applied to the ground, and the resistance to the flow of electric current is measured. Thus the resistivity instrument must comprise both a generator and a detector. It is true that there are *natural* earth currents; these have been utilized for geological prospecting, but they are not suitable for archæological work.

The resistivity of soil and rocks depends on the quantity of water retained in the pores, and electricity is conducted by the process of electrolysis. Hard compact rocks such as granite are very poor conductors, while the more porous limestones are much better, though still poor by comparison with soil, sand and clay. Table 4.1 gives some representative values; the actual resistivities found in practice depend very much on the dampness of the situation.

Table 4.1. Electrical Resistivities of Rocks, Soil and Clay. Representative values expressed in ohm-cm 8 (after Eve and Keys, 1954, p. 104)

Granite	10^9 to 10^{11}	
Sandstone	5×10^9 to 10^{11}	
Limestone (dry)	7×10^4	
Limestone (moist)	4×10^4	
Magnetite	0·6	
Yellow River sand	(0·86% water)	830
Yellow River sand	(9·5% water)	95
Garden soil	(3·3% water)	1670
Garden soil	(17·3% water)	60
Clay	(4·4% water)	1450
Clay	(28% water)	16

While for geological work the finer variations are important, for most archæological applications it is enough to assume that stones and rocks have a very high resistivity compared to soils and clays, and that wide variations will be found among the latter according to their dampness. Consequently stone walls and roads intruding into soil are the archæological features *par excellence* for resistivity surveying, together with earth-filled ditches cut into a rocky substratum. The detectability of other features is variable since local conditions, and particularly geological and climatic variations in water content, may easily mask the effect of archæological features.

4.2   Measurement Techniques

If two metal probes are inserted into the ground, a few feet apart, and a battery is connected between them (see Fig. 4.1) a

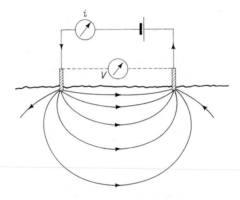

FIG. 4.1. Crude resistivity meter.

small current flows through the ground (of the order of 10^{-2} amp for a 12-V battery). The voltage, V, across the probes, divided by the current, i, gives the total resistance between the probes. The presence between the probes of material having an abnormally high or low resistivity will be shown up by an abnormal value of measured resistance compared to adjacent readings.

This simple system is unsatisfactory for a number of reasons:

(*i*) *Contact Voltages.* There will be small d.c. voltages, of chemical origin, between probes and ground, so that the actual voltage applied to the ground will be different to the measured voltage V. Consequently the measured ratio (V/i) will be affected by variations in contact voltage as well as by variations in resistivity. The effect can be eliminated by using an a.c. generator instead of a battery.

(*ii*) *Contact Resistance.* The resistance between each probe and the soil may be larger than the resistance of the earth itself. This can be avoided by watering the earth in the immediate vicinity of the probe, but the measured resistance then depends on the degree of watering. To avoid the effect of contact resistance, separate probes must be used to measure the voltage, i.e. four probes in all.

(*iii*) *Earth Currents.* Natural earth currents arise from chemical potentials developing between different geological strata and by induction from the transient variations of the earth's magnetic field (see Section 2.2.4). These currents are either d.c. or very low frequency, and effects from them can be avoided by using a.c.; the frequency chosen should not be the same as those of possible man-made earth currents.

(*iv*) *Probe Polarization.* The measured resistance between the probes will increase gradually with the time for which the current is passed. This is a similar effect to electrode polarization in electrolysis and can be avoided by using a.c.

4.2.1   *The Four-Probe Method*

The use of an a.c. power source instead of a battery avoids difficulties (*i*), (*iii*) and (*iv*). Contact resistance effects can be eliminated by using four probes instead of two; the usual arrangement is shown in Fig. 4.2. The voltage appearing across the two

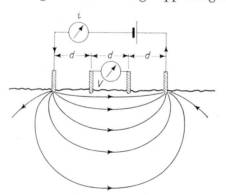

Fig. 4.2. The four-probe method.

detector probes is a small fraction of the total voltage but it is proportional to the current flowing. Thus an effective resistance can be defined by the relation

$$R = \frac{\text{Voltage across detector probes}}{\text{Current through outer probes}} \tag{4.1}$$

Since no current flows through the detector probes, their contact resistance does not matter. The contact resistance of the outer probes affects only the amount of current flowing for a given applied voltage; it does not affect the ratio defined by equation (4.1). The four-probe method by itself avoids difficulties (*ii*) and (*iv*); used with an a.c. power source all four difficulties are eliminated.

The principal reason for equality of spacing between all probes is ease of practical application in making many readings along the same line. Apart from this it is undesirable to make the inner-probe separation much larger than one-third of the outer-probe separation because the reading obtained then becomes more dependent on the length of probe inserted into the ground. On the other hand reduction of the inner-probe separation increases the relative effect of errors in probe position.

It will be shown later (Section 4.4) that for equal spacing the effective resistance R is related to the specific resistivity, ρ, of the earth by the relation

$$\rho = 2\pi d R \tag{4.2}$$

where d is the spacing between probes. If d is measured in feet and R in ohms then

$$\rho = (191 \times d_{\text{ft}} \times R) \text{ ohm-cm} \tag{4.3}$$

The value of ρ obtained is a rough average for the material beneath the inner probes down to a depth of approximately $1.5 \times d$, *as long as it is fairly uniform*. Where the ground consists of two layers of widely differing resistivity, e.g. top-soil above rock, then the lines of current flow are distorted from the paths shown in Fig. 4.2; most of the current will flow along the less resistive top-soil and relations (4.2) and (4.3) are not applicable. Therefore, like magnetic location, the method rests essentially on a comparison of the values measured at different points over the area being surveyed, the location of buried features being indicated by abnormal readings.

4.2.2 The 'Megger'

A common method of measuring resistance is by means of the 'megger', and an adaptation of this instrument* for earth resistance measurements was used in 1946 (Atkinson, 1952, 1953) for the first archæological trial of the technique.

---

* The Megger Earth Tester. Manufactured by Evershed and Vignoles Ltd., Chiswick, London, who publish a useful booklet (No. 245/1) on Geological Resistivity Prospecting.

3*

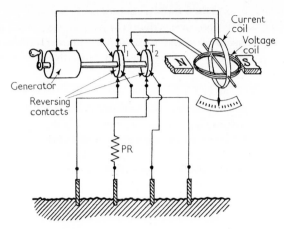

FIG. 4.3. The megger earth tester. T_1 and T_2 are reversing contacts so that although the current in the coils is d.c., the current through the earth is a.c. PR is a protective resistance.

The vital part of a megger consists essentially of two coils rigidly fixed together with their axes perpendicular, pivoted so that they can rotate freely about a third perpendicular axis, and mounted between the poles of a strong permanent magnet. One of the coils is of low resistance and carries the outer-probe current i. The voltage, V, between the two inner probes is applied to the second coil, which is of high resistance, and a small current flows which is proportional to V. Each coil is equivalent to a short bar magnet of moment proportional to the current flowing in it (and also to the number of turns), so that the direction of the resultant depends on the ratio of V to i; since the pair of coils is free to rotate as a whole, an equilibrium position is taken up with the resultant along the lines of force of the permanent magnet. A pointer fixed onto the coils indicates the ratio of V to i directly in ohms.

Since the pointer indicates a *ratio*, its position is not affected by variations in the applied voltage; this is provided by a hand-turned d.c. generator. Although the current in the coils must be d.c., the current through the ground must be a.c. if effects (*i*) and (*iii*) are to be avoided. This is achieved by two reversing contacts T_1 and T_2 (see Fig. 4.3) driven from the same shaft as the generator. T_2 converts the generator voltage to a.c. before application to the outer probes, and T_1 rectifies the a.c. voltage across the inner probes before application to the voltage coil. PR is a protective resistance to avoid damage to the voltage coil. When the hand-generator is turned at the recommended speed of 135 rev/min, the a.c. voltage across the outer probes is about 200 V (at 40 c/s) on open circuit; unless the probe handles are carefully insulated, the operator moving the probes must keep a careful eye on the man turning the generator! Plate XVI shows the 'megger' set up for field use.

PLATE XVI. Resistivity surveying—the megger.

Compared to the instruments described next, the megger has the advantage that the operator (in addition to turning the handle) needs only to read the pointer position and no mental judgement of a 'null' is required. As a method it has the disadvantage that, since a small current is drawn from the inner probes to energize the voltage coil, a high contact resistance at these probes can upset the reading; this can be a serious drawback in dry conditions. It is overcome in the Geophysical Megger Earth Tester by employing a null balancing technique; since this is similar in principle to the next method, the reader is referred elsewhere (e.g. Eve and Keys, 1954, p. 119) for details.

4.2.3 Null Balancing Methods

Fig. 4.4 illustrates the principle. The outer-probe current passes through a low resistance S, and the voltage developed across S is compared, via the transformer T, with the inner-probe voltage.

S is adjusted until the detector deflection is zero, and from the setting of S the effective inner probe resistance (as defined by equation (4.1)) is deduced.

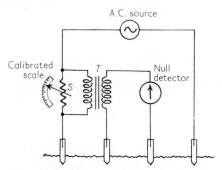

Fig. 4.4. Null balancing circuit. The calibrated rheostat S is adjusted until the voltage across the transformer secondary exactly balances the voltage developed across the inner probes.

In the 'Tellohm' Soil Resistance Meter* the a.c. voltage is generated by a reversing-relay (110 c/s) driven from a 30-V dry battery. A second set of contacts on the relay provides synchronous rectification of the difference between the transformer output voltage and the inner-probe voltage so that a sensitive d.c. galvanometer can be used as the null detector. Plate XVII shows the instrument as used by the United Kingdom Ministry of Works Test Branch; a board attached to the instrument stand enables the readings to be recorded in plan-form directly.

An alternative type of instrument, the M–C Resistivity Meter,† employs a transistorized oscillator for the outer-probe current and meter indication from the rectified output of an amplifier for null detection. The instrument runs from a 4·5-V torch battery and can be held in the palm of the hand (see Plate XVIII). The frequency employed is 500 c/s; this has the disadvantage that in very high resistance ground, capacitative effects can become important (see Section 4.4.6), resulting in a phase difference between the transformer voltage and the inner probe voltage. As a consequence the null position of S, as indicated by the minimum reading on the meter, becomes less precise. However, trouble from this cause is not to be expected except on very rocky ground, and it is not a significant limitation for archæological use. The convenience of its small size (4·7 in. × 3·7 in. × 3·2 in.) is a very great advantage.

* Manufactured by Nash and Thompson Ltd., Chessington, Surrey, England.
† Manufactured by Martin-Clark Instruments, Farnham Road, Guildford, Surrey, England.

(*Ph.:* M. J. Aitken)

PLATE XVII. Resistivity surveying—the 'Tellohm'. Set up for use with the multi-electrode system employed by the United Kingdom Ministry of Works Test Branch.

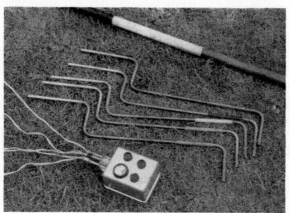

(*Permission from Martin-Clark Instruments Ltd.*)

PLATE XVIII. Resistivity surveying—the M–C Meter. The probes are cranked for ease of insertion and withdrawal. The leads leave the instrument via the rotary switch on the left-hand side. The scale interval shown is 1 ft.

4.2.4   *The Equipotential Method*

This is an alternative to the four-probe technique; the only use of it reported so far (De Terra, Romero and Stewart, 1949) has been in connection with the discovery of the Tepexpan man in Mexico in 1948. The current is passed through the ground between two parallel extended electrodes consisting of a number of probes linked together. These two electrodes are fixed some distance apart and the change of potential in the ground between is investigated by a pair of roving probes connected to headphones. Lines of equal potential are plotted out; in the absence of any underground disturbance these are parallel. A distorted pattern indicates the presence of a buried feature in the centre of the distorted region.

Appreciable electrical power is required so that the generator is rather heavy and cumbersome. Another disadvantage is that the greater distance between the current electrodes, compared to the four-probe method, leads to a greater depth of penetration in the ground; consequently geological features will show up more strongly than archæological ones. Close spacing of the outer electrodes is not practicable.

4.3   Field Application

4.3.1   *Procedure*

Measurements are made along a series of traverses, each 50 to 100 ft long and parallel to one another. The probes are inserted along the line of a traverse (marked out with a measuring tape) and moved along it as readings are taken. The probe ensemble is moved by a distance equal to the probe separation for each new reading and in this way a resistivity profile, such as those shown in Figs. 4.5 and 4.6, is obtained.

The probes themselves are sharpened $\frac{1}{4}$ in. to $\frac{1}{2}$ in. mild-steel rods and they are each connected to a terminal on the instrument by a suitable length of single-core cable. For equation (4.1) to be obeyed precisely, the length of probe in the ground should be not more than one-twentieth of the probe separation; in practice this can be exceeded as long as the length in the ground is kept constant by means of a suitable stop. The probe separation employed should be roughly equal to the expected depth of the feature; if the separation is too great the feature forms only a small fraction of the volume penetrated by the current, if the separation is too small very little current will reach the feature.

For speed of operation a system of five probes is used. These are connected into the instrument by means of a rotary switch, which is advanced by one step before each measurement. Each probe is then successively, outer, spare, outer, inner, inner; in this way only one probe needs moving for each new measurement and this can be done by the probe-mover while the operator is taking the reading. The rotary switch is designed so that twists in the cabling do not accumulate.

An alternative system, used by the United Kingdom Ministry of Works Test Branch, employs a dozen or so probes each connected to a terminal on a multi-bank switch on the instrument (see Plate XVII); this successively energizes consecutive sets of four probes down the line. When a probe has served its purpose on one traverse it is moved to a corresponding position on the parallel traverse adjacent. Although the amount of cabling is considerable, the system is well worthwhile for extensive surveys over open ground.

Quite rapid ground coverage is possible with either system. Well-trained operators can take about ten readings per minute; if the time for laying out traverses is included the average rate is about 300 readings per hour. This corresponds to a rate of ground coverage approaching that of magnetic surveying; however, it is difficult to keep up top-speed for many hours because of the mental strain involved in correct probe-movement (with the five-probe system) and reading taking (with a null-balancing instrument). Mechanization of probe-movement is difficult. Rigid mounting of the probes on a frame is impracticable on account of the variable pressure needed to insert the probes. An alternative possibility is to fix the probes on a sort of caterpillar-track but the practical difficulties are considerable; it is questionable whether the complication involved is warranted.

4.3.2 *Types of Feature Detectable*

Fig. 4.5 shows the resistivity profile resulting from a wall, together with the corresponding magnetic profile for comparison. The resistivity is expressed in ohm-metre, calculated from the measured resistance by means of equation (4.3). As expected, walls show up strongly. The violent fluctuations in resistance when the inner probes are over the wall are characteristic of wall-detection, and a clear-cut inverted W is evident. An effect of this type has been noted by Tagg (1957) in laboratory model measurements, and he attributes it to distortion of the current path by the proximity of the feature to the individual probes.

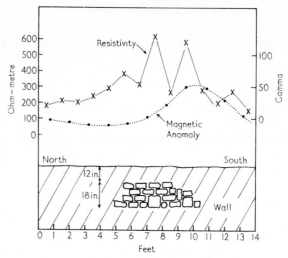

FIG. 4.5. Resistivity profile—wall. The resistivity scale is on the left and the magnetic on the right. Resistivity probe separation was 1 ft., magnetic detector-bottle height above ground was 1 ft. The displacement of the magnetic anomaly to the south is explained in Chapter 2.

Comprehensive resistivity surveys involving walls and building foundations have been carried out by Atkinson at Old Windsor, and by Clark at Cunetio, Wiltshire (Annable, 1958) among others.

Earth-filled ditches usually produce a low resistance (see Fig. 4.6) on account of the low resistivity of the damp filling. The effect

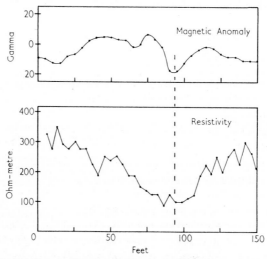

FIG. 4.6. Resistivity profile—Inner Fosse at Verulamium. Resistivity probe spacing: 4 ft. Magnetic detector-bottle height: 3 ft.

is greatly attenuated if the filling has dried out so as to acquire a humidity comparable to that of the surrounding strata. If the upper layers of the filling contain an appreciable amount of stone an anomalously *high* resistance may be produced, particularly when the probe separation is such as to make the measurement most sensitive at the depth of the stone layer. In the first archæological trial of the technique the three concentric ditches of a Neolithic camp were plotted out (Atkinson, 1952) with remarkable precision, together with a number of pits, to which the same considerations apply.

Empty tombs and caverns show up as a high resistance owing to the absence of a conducting medium. Etruscan tombs have been detected by Lerici (1959) and an underground cavern at a depth of 150 ft (using comparable probe separations) by Palmer (1959).

A remarkable campaign of surveys has been undertaken by Tagg (1957) with the object of locating the royal treasure lost by King John in 1216. The treasure was lost when an exceptionally high tide swept the royal baggage train from the causeway on which it was crossing the Wash estuary. The area concerned is now dry land; no visible trace of the causeway remains but evidence for its position has been obtained from the resistivity measurements. It is hypothesized that the causeway followed a natural bank formed by a rise in the clay bed that is elsewhere covered by 40 ft of sand; since the resistivity of the sand concerned is a little higher than the clay this bank could be detected. The usual four-probe method was followed in the field, employing a 60-ft probe separation and using the 'megger'. The position of the treasure along the course of the bank is still unknown, and it is unlikely that the relative size of such metal parts as remain will be sufficient to produce an abnormal resistance reading, despite their high conductivity. Electromagnetic methods (see Section 4.5) can be valuable in such circumstances.

4.3.3 *Handicaps*

Two geological effects are serious. Firstly, natural pockets of clay or soil in a rocky sub-stratum may easily be mistaken for archæological features, as is also the case with near-surface streams. Secondly, if the top-soil contains rocky-rubble, as frequently occurs on limestone, the random fluctuations of the resistance measurements may mask any features. In extremely stony ground the method may be impossible simply because of the difficulty of inserting the probes.

Heavy rain precludes operation because the surface water short-circuits the probes. A moderately damp soil may be beneficial when looking for walls, but it is a drawback for ditches and pits since the resistivity contrast is reduced. If only the upper layer of soil has been dampened by rain, a greater proportion of the current will travel near the surface thereby reducing the depth of detectable feature. Conversely a high water-table may attenuate the effect of near-surface features; a subtle way of avoiding this difficulty is to carry out measurements during weather cold enough for the water to be frozen solid (Hampl and Fritsch, 1959).

4.4   Theory

As with magnetic location, buried features are revealed by abnormalities in closely-spaced readings taken over the area concerned. If anything the method is more empirical than in the magnetic case, because even if the resistivities of the component parts of a feature are known, a theoretical computation of the resulting measured resistance is hopelessly complex, mainly because of the distortion of the lines of current flow. However, some acquaintance with the elementary theory applicable to ground of uniform resistivity is a helpful basis for field experience, and also, in designing a suitable instrument, some knowledge of the orders of magnitude of the electrical quantities concerned is necessary.

4.4.1   *Single Probe*

The current from a single probe inserted in ground of uniform resistivity and maintained at a potential of $+V_0$, by means of a

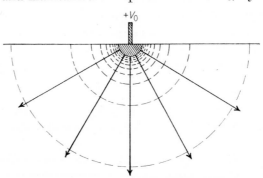

Fig. 4.7. Current flow from single probe. The probe has been idealized by representing it as a hemispherical boss. In practice the probe ends in a point; this distorts the flow pattern close to it but not at large distances. The dotted lines represent equipotentials.

battery of which the earth-return is distant from the probe, flows in straight radial lines as shown in Fig. 4.7. The equipotentials are hemispherical surfaces so that at a radius r the current crossing unit area of such a surface is given by j, where

$$j = \frac{i}{2\pi r^2} \qquad (4.4)$$

and i is the total current leaving the probe. Since j is related to the electric field E at any point by the relation

$$j = \frac{E}{\rho} \qquad (4.5)$$

it follows that

$$E = \frac{\rho i}{2\pi r^2} \qquad (4.6)$$

where ρ is the resistivity.

Hence, by integration, the potential at any radius r is given by

$$V = \frac{\rho i}{2\pi r} \qquad (4.7)$$

If we assume the end of the probe is a hemisphere of radius r_0, of which the flat surface is flush with the ground, then we must have

$$V_0 = \frac{\rho i}{2\pi r_0} \qquad (4.8)$$

where V_0 is the potential of the probe.

Since this relates the current flowing to the applied potential, it defines a probe resistance equal to $(\rho/2\pi r_0)$.

4.4.2   Two Probes

The flow of current between two probes *differing* in potential by V_0 may be considered as the superposition of the flow patterns for two isolated probes at $+\frac{1}{2}V_0$ and $-\frac{1}{2}V_0$ respectively, as long as r_0 is negligible compared to the distance between the probes. The actual current at any point is the vector resultant of the individual currents (see Fig. 4.8) and the potential is the algebraic sum of the individual potentials. In this way the current patterns of Figs. 4.1 and 4.2 may be derived. All the current flowing into the earth from the positive probe flows out of the earth at the negative

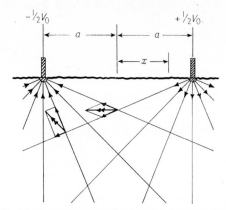

Fig. 4.8. Current flow from two probes. The magnitude and direction of the current at any point is obtained by vector addition of the currents that would flow from a positive probe and a negative probe independently of each other (see Fig. 4.7). This does not apply close to either probe.

probe, so that from equation (4.8) the resistance between the probes is given by

$$R_0 = \frac{\rho}{\pi r_0} \qquad (4.9)$$

Although R_0 is independent of the distance between the probes, this is not a good method of measuring ρ, firstly because of the additional variable contact resistance that will be encountered in practice, secondly because in deriving equation (4.9) it has been assumed that the probes have hemispherical ends just protruding into the ground—an impracticable arrangement—and thirdly because the main part of the resistance is that of the earth very close to the probe.

When using the four-probe method, R_0 is only of interest in determining a suitable value for the output impedance of the power source used. In practice the portion of the probe in the ground is not hemispherical, but consists of two or three inches of rod ending in a sharpened point. In this case one can define r'_0, the effective value of r_0 which when substituted in equation (4.9) gives the observed value of R_0. For $\frac{5}{16}$ in. diameter rod, r'_0 is about 2 cm for 2 in. of rod in the ground, and 4 cm for 6 in. These figures do not increase much if a $\frac{1}{2}$ in. rod is used instead.

4.4.3   Voltage Variation between Two Probes

The potential at any point on the ground surface along the line joining the two probes, distant x from the mid-point, can be obtained from equation (4.7) and is given by,

$$V = \frac{\rho i}{2\pi} \left\{ \frac{1}{(a-x)} - \frac{1}{(a+x)} \right\}$$ (4.10)

$$= \frac{\rho i}{\pi a} \left\{ \frac{x/a}{1-(x/a)^2} \right\}$$

where $2a$ is the distance between the probes.

Figure 4.9 shows the variation of V along the line between the probes; the potential changes rapidly in the vicinity of the probes. In the central section the change is small but uniform. The potential difference, V_1, between two inner probes placed at $x = +b$, and $x = -b$, is given by

$$V_1 = \frac{2\rho i}{\pi a} \left\{ \frac{b/a}{1-(b/a)^2} \right\}$$ (4.11)

from equation (4.10.) Thus the inner probe resistance, defined as (V_1/i), is given by

$$R_1 = \frac{2\rho}{\pi a} \left\{ \frac{b/a}{1-(b/a)^2} \right\}$$ (4.12)

This depends only on ρ and the spacings between the probes. Although the actual amount of current flowing will depend very much on the resistivity of the ground very close to the outer probes, the value of R_1 obtained is mainly dependent on the region below the centre probes, down to a depth somewhat greater than the inner probe spacing.

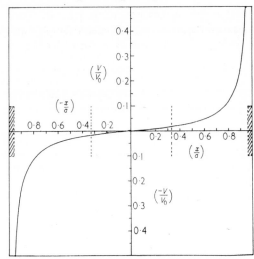

FIG. 4.9. Potential along line joining two probes. The probe potentials are $+V_0$ and $-V_0$ respectively. The separation is $2a$. V is the potential at a distance x from the mid-point. The probe ends are assumed to be hemispherical and of radius $r_0 = (a/20)$.

If b equals $(a/3)$, the probes are equally spaced, in which case

$$R_1 = \frac{3\rho}{4\pi a}$$

On substituting d for the inter-probe distance $(2a/3)$, the relation (4.2) quoted in Section 4.2.1 is obtained, viz:

$$R_1 = \frac{\rho}{2\pi d} \qquad (4.2)$$

4.4.4   Error due to Finite Probe Insertion

The foregoing assumes that the length of probe in the ground is negligible. Wenner (1916) has shown that for probes inserted to a depth h but *insulated except at their ends*, the inner probe resistance is given by

$$R_1 = \frac{\rho}{4\pi d}\left[1 + \frac{2}{\{1+(4h^2/d^2)\}^{1/2}} - \frac{1}{\{1+(h^2/d^2)\}^{1/2}}\right] \qquad (4.13)$$

This reduces to (4.2) for $h \ll d$. The practical case, in which current can leave the probes all along the length inserted, will be intermediate between equations (4.2) and (4.13). Since the difference between these is less than 7 per cent as long as h is less than one-fifth of d, the effect may be neglected except when the spacing is only 1 ft, and even then, for comparative purposes it is unimportant as long as h is kept fairly constant.

Using an inter-probe separation (d) of 1 ft, and $\frac{5}{16}$ in. diameter probes, the measured resistance, R_1, decreases by 10 per cent on changing the length of probe inserted from 2 in. to 6 in. On the other hand with an inter-probe separation of 2 ft, the corresponding decrease is less than 2 per cent.

4.4.5   Errors due to Inaccurate Probe Spacing

It follows from equation (4.12) that a certain percentage error in the inner-probe separation, $2b$, produces an error of the same percentage in R_1, and a certain percentage error in the outer-probe separation, $2a$, produces an error of double that percentage, but in the opposite sense. Hence when the nominal inter-probe distance, d, is only 1 ft, a positive error of 1 in. in the inner-probe separation will cause R_1 to be too high by 8 per cent and a positive error of 1 in. in the outer-probe separation will cause R_1 to be too low by 5·5 per cent. For a nominal inter-probe distance of 2 ft, the corresponding figures are 4 per cent and 3 per cent. When using the smaller spacing, the probes must be inserted to within $\frac{1}{2}$ in.

of their correct positions in order to keep the total error in R_1 below 14 per cent.

Errors due to lateral displacements of the probes from a straight line are comparatively unimportant.

4.4.6 *Capacitative Effects and Phase Shift*

By a similar analysis to that in Sections 4.4.1 etc. it can be shown that the inner-probe capacity C_1 defined similarly to R_1 is given by the relation

$$C_1 = \left(\frac{\rho k}{4\pi} \times \frac{10^{-9}}{R_1} \right) \text{ farads}$$

where k is the dielectric constant. Hence if θ is the phase lag of the inner-probe voltage behind the outer-probe current when the a.c. frequency is f c/s, its value is given by

$$\tan \theta = \frac{\frac{1}{2} f \rho k}{10^9} \tag{4.14}$$

Taking $f = 500$ c/s, and $k = 5$, θ will be less than $5°$ as long as ρ does not exceed 6×10^4 ohm-cm. Table 4.1 indicates that this figure may be exceeded on rocky ground where the top-soil is thin, and in such circumstances the null position will not be sharply defined unless compensating condensers are used to correct the phase shift. With the Tellohm, $f = 110$ c/s, the resistivity can be five times greater before a given phase shift is reached, and with the 'megger' ($f = 40$ c/s), ten times greater.

4.5 Electromagnetic Surveying

Probe insertion is a tedious business, particularly for geological prospecting where the spacing must be several hundred feet in order to penetrate deeply enough. A method widely used in geological work avoids the use of probes by measuring the effective reflection coefficient of the ground for fairly low frequency electromagnetic waves (down to 500 c/s). The source of these is a transmitter coil carried by one operator, and any variation in the phase and the amplitude of the signal picked up by a receiver coil carried by another operator several hundred feet away, indicates variations in the resistivity of the sub-strata, thereby showing up the presence of ore-bodies.

The depth of penetration of electromagnetic waves is given

roughly by

$$d = 5 \times 10^3 \sqrt{(\rho/f)} \qquad (4.15)$$

where ρ is the resistivity in ohm-cm, and f is the frequency in cycles per second. Consequently, to restrict the depth to regions of archæological interest a frequency in the range of 10 kc to 1 Mc could be used.

The author is unaware of any comprehensive trial of this technique for general archæological use; it seems possible that on the small scale necessary surface irregularities would mask anything except non-metallic features within a few inches of the surface, and deeper-lying metal objects of appreciable size. Metal detectors, developments of the war-time mine-detector, are of course widely used by treasure hunters, and are obtainable commercially.* For a superior instrument of this type the range claimed by the makers varies from 9 in. for a 1-in. diameter coin, to 20 ft for a metal plate 5 ft by 5 ft. Regrettably such finds are too rare an archæological event to warrant surveys with this technique. On the other hand a metal detector is a useful method of obtaining prior warning of small metal objects during actual excavation, of a grave for example.

References

Annable, F. K., 1958: Excavation and field-work in Wiltshire; 1958. *Wiltsh. archaeol. nat. Hist. Mag.*, **207**, 233

Atkinson, R. J. C., 1952: *La Découverte du Passé* (ed. A. Laming), Picard, Paris, p. 63

Atkinson, R. J. C., 1953: *Field Archaeology*, 2nd edn., Methuen, London, p. 32

De Terra, H., Romero, J. and Stewart, T. D., 1949: Tepexpan man. *Viking Fund Publications in Anthropology*, No. 11, New York

Eve, A. S. and Keys, D. A., 1954: *Applied Geophysics*, 4th edn., Cambridge University Press

Hampl, F. and Fritsch, V., 1959: Geoelektrische Messungen in ihrer Anwendung für die Archäologie. *Technische Beiträge zur Archäologie, Mainz*, **1**, 116

Lerici, C. M., Bartoccini, R. and Moretti, M., 1959: Necropoli di Tarquinia. *Fondazione Ing. C. M. Lerici, publication*, No. 15, Milan

Palmer, L. S., 1959: Examples of geoelectric surveys. *Proc. Instn. elec. Engrs*, **106A**

Tagg, G. F., 1957: A resistivity survey in the Wash area. *J. Instn. elec. Engrs*, **3**, 5

Wenner, F., 1916: A method of measuring earth resistivity, *Bull. U.S. Bur. of Stand.*, **12**, 469

* For example, Frazar and Hansen Ltd., 301 Clay Street, San Francisco 11. Fisher Research Laboratory Ltd., 1272 W. Pender Street, Vancouver. Rank Cintel Ltd., Worsley Bridge Road, Lower Sydenham, London S.E. 26.

CHAPTER 5

DATING

'How old is it?' is the inevitable question that greets the discovery of any ancient relic. The older it is, the greater its fascination and any method of dating carries immense popular esteem. To the archæologist the date is a vital part of the information he is seeking to retrieve—Sir Mortimer Wheeler has compared archæology without dates to a train time-table without times. Yet a time-table which shows only the order in which the trains run is better than no time-table at all—one could tell, for instance, whether passengers from the branch line can catch the express. So too when *absolute* dates in years A.D. or B.C. are not available; *relative* dating of events can throw valuable light on how and why certain developments took place, whether they are cultural, technical or political. Absolute dating is obviously more desirable since it can establish contemporaneity between widely separated civilizations and enable a world-wide picture to be built up. It is essential if the *pace* of cultural or technical development is to be determined.

Archæological dating is usually taken to mean the process by which the date of remains found on one site is inferred from the close association, of a particular type of implement or pottery found there, with objects of known date on some other site. These may be coins or written evidence, and usually a lot of steps intervene. The archæological chronology of the Neolithic Age in Europe is ultimately based on historical records in the Near East. Prior to historical records, or where there are weak links in the chain of successive association, the archæologist must be content with relative dating; or else in some way make use of natural time-dependent processes. Some of these are outlined in the present chapter; radiocarbon dating and magnetic dating are discussed in more detail in Chapters 6 and 7.

The ways in which an object may retain evidence of its age are subtle and unexpected. No doubt many new techniques will be evolved in the future. For magnetic dating and to some extent for radiocarbon dating, it is essential that the specimen should be available in its original position rather than on a museum shelf

79

(always assuming it has not been thrown away as valueless). This may also be true of future methods, thus powerfully reinforcing the conscientious archæologist's plea that something should be left for future generations and moderation exercised in what is excavated today.

5.1   Tree-Ring Counting (*Dendrochronology*)

The significance of the annual growth rings in the cross-section of a tree has been realized for a long time and the first archæological application was made in 1811. Wet summers produce thick rings and dry summers narrow ones. Consequently a distinctive sequence in annual rainfalls is reflected as a distinctive sequence in terms of the thickness of the annual rings. This makes it possible to carry the dating back through several generations of trees; starting with a recently-felled tree, a distinctive group of early rings is matched to the corresponding group in an earlier tree and so on. In this way Douglass (1929) was able to establish the prehistoric chronology of pueblo Indian dwelling sites in Arizona, showing that the earliest may have originated 1900 years ago. The technique has also been applied in Scandinavia, Central Europe and Britain. Attempts have been made to show that the same distinctive sequences occur in European trees as occur in America; this is termed '*teleconnexion*' but on the present evidence it seems doubtful whether a dated range of sequences established on one continent can reliably be used on another. However, once the range of sequences has been built up for a particular region the method is a very powerful one for types of archæological remains that still carry beams and timbers. The reader is referred to Zeuner (1958) for a critical account of the technique. An interesting observation is the occurrence of 11-year cycles in tree-ring thicknesses, corresponding to the 11-year sun-spot cycles.

Tree-rings are of immense value for radiocarbon dating. They provide samples of known date which are highly suitable for that technique; the carbon atoms in the cellulose of the wood remain fixed once the ring is formed and that date of formation is the date deduced from the radiocarbon measurement.

5.2   Varve Counting

Analogous to tree-rings are the annual varves (i.e. layers) found in clays that originated in the beds of lakes dammed-up by glaciers. During the summer, melting is more rapid than in winter and the sediment deposited is thicker and coarser. Conversely to tree-rings, a hot, dry summer is represented by an exceptionally thick varve. Varve sequences are recognizable in the same way as with tree-rings and the method has been extensively applied in Sweden by de Geer, who commenced his investigations in 1878. The most important application has been the establishment (de Geer, 1940) of absolute chronology of the end of the last Ice Age (the 'Late-Glacial' period) in Northern Europe—about 12000 years ago. This chronology has provided an extremely valuable check of radiocarbon dating back as far as that time (refer, for example, to Wright, 1957). For further information about the techniques and results of varve dating the reader is again referred to Zeuner (1958). As with tree-rings correlation with sun-spot cycles has been found.

Varves acquire a remanent magnetism on deposition. This provides a link with magnetic dating, but unfortunately it is of limited value owing to the unsatisfactory nature of the samples for precise work (see Section 7.8).

5.3 Radioactive Methods

Radioactive decay is an immutable process, independent of external conditions. Consequently it is an ideal basis for absolute dating. In a given time a radioactive isotope decays by a certain fraction of the amount remaining; the decay rate is usually specified in terms of the *half-life*—the time required for one half of a given initial quantity of the isotope to decay away.

5.3.1 *Geological Methods*

By successive stages of radioactive decay uranium-238 forms lead-206. The effective half-life is 4560 million years. By measuring the amount of lead-206 relative to uranium-238 in a rock, the time of formation can be deduced—the older the rock the greater the lead content. Other pairs of 'parents' and 'daughters' are:

uranium-235 to lead-207, half-life 710 million years
thorium-232 to lead-208, half-life 13900 million years
rubidium-87 to strontium-87, half-life 60000 million years
potassium-40 to argon-40, half-life 1330 million years.

Lead of non-radioactive origin has an atomic weight of 204; the various isotopes of lead can be distinguished by means of a *mass spectrometer*.

Another method is to measure the helium content of the rock relative to the uranium and thorium content. In the course of radioactive decay helium is produced in the form of alpha particles, so that the older the rock the greater the helium content. The rate of helium production can be calculated from a knowledge of the radioactive decay scheme. A difficulty with this method is that some rocks are sufficiently porous for part of the helium to escape.

In all these methods the radioisotopes concerned are naturally occurring elements present in the earth's crust at its formation. One does not expect these to be of archæological interest for, by definition, any with a half-life comparable to archæological ages (half a million years at the most) will have completely disappeared (since the age of the earth is greater than 4000 million years). One exception is the *ionium* method, applicable to carefully selected deep-ocean sediments (Volchok and Kulp, 1957). Direct archæological application is hardly likely but it is of interest (within the context of this book) firstly as a cross check of the validity of the carbon-14 method (see Section 6.4.1) and secondly as a method of dating geological changes of the past 400 000 years (e.g. the later Ice Ages), which can in turn be linked with the early development of Man. The half-life of ionium is only 83 000 years, but it is continually formed in sea-water (as well as in rocks) by the radioactive decay of uranium. It is preferentially deposited in ocean sediments, where, because it is no longer 'supported' by uranium, its concentration decreases according to its own half-life, rather than the half-life of uranium. Its presence is detected by measuring the radium concentration; ionium decays to radium and since the latter's half-life of 1600 years is short compared to the ionium half-life, the radium concentration is proportional to the ionium concentration. The main difficulty with the method is that the sediment must be deposited in undisturbed conditions and the mineralogical composition must be uniform over the thickness concerned. This restriction is being overcome by the simultaneous measurement of one of the decay products of protoactinium (Pa^{231}_{91}). This is deposited along with ionium (Th^{230}_{90}) but its half-life is only 32 000 years. Consequently, the ratio of the decay products of ionium and of protoactinium is a measure of the age of the sediment independent of the rate of deposition.

Another geological method of increasing archæological interest is potassium–argon dating. Despite the long half-life, with very sensitive measuring techniques it has been possible to detect the minute quantities of argon that have accumulated in volcanic lavas originating during archæological times (Evernden, Curtis and Kistler, 1957). This technique appears to hold higher promise than the ionium method for indirect, but absolute, dating up to

the time when the radiocarbon method becomes applicable—
70 000 years ago at the very most.

For further information about geological dating methods the
reader is referred to Rankama (1954), Faul (1954), Ahrens (1956),
Jacobs, Russell and Wilson (1959), Tilton and Davis (1959), and
Russell and Farquhar (1960).

5.3.2   *Radiocarbon Dating*

The half-life of carbon-14 is 5570 years and it is continually
formed in the upper atmosphere due to cosmic ray bombardment.
It becomes uniformly distributed throughout the living plant and
animal world. In dead material the carbon-14 content gradually
decreases due to radioactive decay. By comparing the carbon-14
content of a sample with the carbon-14 content of a living sample
the time elapsed since death can be deduced.

Although the radioactive decay process is immutable there are
certain other factors which give rise to inaccuracies. These are discussed in the next chapter; it seems likely that there will always be
a residual uncertainty of at least ± 100 years, so that prehistory
will remain its most important field of application. The most
suitable types of specimen are charcoal and well-preserved wood.
Unfortunately bone often gives unreliable results.

Another long-lived radioisotope produced by cosmic ray bombardment is beryllium-10. This has a half-life of 2·5 million years
and has been detected in deep ocean sediments. It seems unlikely
that it will be a satisfactory dating isotope (see Section 6.6).

5.4   Magnetic Dating

The time-dependent quantity in this case is the direction of the
earth's magnetic field. As already explained in Chapter 2 a record
of this is retained in baked clay. Unfortunately the variation does
not follow any predictable law and calibration from samples of
known date is first necessary. Another difficulty is that this calibration holds only for a region about 500 miles across. On the
other hand the method is potentially capable of a much higher
precision than radiocarbon dating and consequently its most useful
contribution will be during more recent times—the last 2000 years.

The intensity of the earth's magnetic field varies as well, but on
a much longer time scale. The intensity variation is a grosser effect
than the directional change and may be world-wide instead of
regional. Further investigation is needed before assessing the
feasibility of using the intensity variation for dating. Such data is

also of interest, not only in connection with radiocarbon dating (see Section 6.4.1) but also for the light it throws on the mechanism by which the earth's magnetic field is produced.

5.5 Pollen Analysis

The general climate of a region is reflected in the types of tree which flourish there. Hence information about past climates can be obtained from microscopic identification of tree-pollen which is retained in stratigraphic sequence in peat bogs. Following the last Ice Age several widespread climatic variations took place. These have been related to varve and radiocarbon chronologies so that archæological remains found associated with a given pollen 'zone' can be dated in this way. Boundaries between zones are separated by several thousand years after 5000 B.C. but before that, closer in time to the last Ice Age, climatic changes were more rapid and distinguishable changes sometimes occurred in less than a thousand years.

Zeuner (1958) gives a full account of the application of pollen analysis.

5.6 Relative Dating

It is questionable whether or not the last two techniques should be included under this heading. However, although they are both secondary methods in the sense of needing prior 'calibration', they do record an external, widespread change—the earth's magnetism, and the earth's climate respectively. In the methods to be mentioned now the time-dependent property is internal—which was also the case with radiocarbon dating—but the time-variation is not independent of the conditions which the sample has experienced.

5.6.1 *Analytical Dating of Bone: Fluorine, Uranium and Nitrogen*

Radiocarbon dating is often unreliable when applied to bone samples. In any case the radiocarbon method is restricted to the last 70000 years, and consequently the period covering the anthropological development of man, when bone-dating would be of particular value, is outside its range. However, relative dating of bones found in the same deposit can be accomplished by measuring the fluorine, uranium or nitrogen contents (Oakley, 1954). Old bones can be distinguished from later intrusions, and these techniques were used in showing that the Piltdown Man was a hoax.

Fluorine and uranium are gradually acquired by bone through alteration of the phosphatic mineral (*hydroxyapatite*) of which bones are mainly composed. The rate of acquisition depends on the fluorine and uranium contents of the ground-water which has percolated through the deposits; in limestone cave deposits, for instance, the fluorine content of ancient bones is anomalously low. The fluorine content is determined by chemical analysis; the advantage of using uranium is that the content can be determined from the radioactivity (extremely small) of the specimen, so that the method is potentially non-destructive.

The nitrogen content of bone decreases with prolonged burial. This is due to the gradual disappearance of protein (collagen); the rate depends on external conditions, and where the soil is permanently frozen or where bacteria and air are excluded (e.g. by burial in clay), it may persist indefinitely.

The degree of variation occurring in the concentrations of these three elements is illustrated in Table 5.1, derived from Oakley, 1954. The accepted ages would be roughly as follows: the Neolithic skull 4000–5000 years, the Swanscombe skull 300000 years and the elephant molar 600000 years or more. Included also in Table 5.1 are the analyses for the jawbone and skull of the Piltdown

Table 5.1. Fluorine, nitrogen and uranium contents of fossil bones (after Oakley, 1954)

	Fluorine, %	Nitrogen, %	Uranium oxide, ppm[a]
Fresh bone	0·03	4·0	0
Neolithic skull, Kent	0·3	1·9	1
Swanscombe skull	1·7	nil	27
Ichkeul *Elephas* cf. *planifrons* molar	2·7	trace	580
Piltdown jawbone	0·03	3·9	0
Piltdown skull	0·1	1·4	2

[a] *Note:* ppm = parts per million.

Man. Taken alone the low fluorine content might be explicable because of low fluorine content of the ground-water in the gravel concerned, but coupled with low uranium and high nitrogen contents the evidence is strong that the jawbone was of modern origin and the skull very much later than had been claimed. There was other corroborative evidence too, among it the analytical deduction (see Section 8.4) that the jawbone had been artificially stained to look old.

5.6.2   *Ultrasonic Dating of Bone*

Specht and Berg (1959) have shown that the velocity of sound in bone decreases with age. Unfortunately the time-scale is logarithmic so that although the velocity in bone 500 years old is half that of modern bone, and so easily distinguishable, the velocity only falls to one quarter of the present-day value for 5000-year old bone. It seems likely that the most valuable application of the method will be in establishing the authenticity of supposedly ancient bone in museums—for the method is potentially non-destructive.

5.7   Thermoluminescent Dating

The damage caused by nuclear radiation to living animal cells is well known. Inanimate matter is affected too, and in minerals strains and distortions are set up in the crystal structure. Such *radiation damage* occurs naturally through prolonged exposure to the alpha particles emitted by the thorium and uranium which is present to a minute concentration (on the average 10 and 2 grams per ton respectively) in most rocks. The same holds for clay minerals. If the temperature is raised the strains of radiation damage are released; this happens when clay is baked. Consequently the radiation damage in pottery accumulates anew from the time of baking and can therefore be used to measure age.

Radiation damage can be detected by measuring the minute amount of visible light that is emitted if the temperature is raised by several hundred degrees centigrade; this light represents the energy released as the distortions of the crystal structure disappear. It can be measured by means of a photomultiplier. The light output is dependent not only on the time since previous heating but also on the uranium content of the clay and on the susceptibility to damage. Consequently it is necessary firstly to measure the natural alpha radioactivity of the specimen, and secondly to measure the damage produced by bombardment with a known quantity of radiation from an artificial source. Suitable apparatus for measurement has been described by Lewis, Whitaker and Chapman (1959).

The method was primarily used (e.g. Zeller, 1951) in determining the age of carbonate rocks, but the results were unreliable owing to the influence of impurities, particularly iron. Archæological application, to pottery samples, is currently being made at the University of California by Kennedy (1960) and the initial results are highly encouraging. The method would have the advantage over radiocarbon dating that pottery is much more common than samples suitable for the latter method; nor would there be the necessity, so important (but also so restrictive) in magnetic dating, for the samples to be found *in situ*. The sample is destroyed in the process of measurement, but a fragment of only a few square inches may be all that is required.

References

Ahrens, L. H., 1956: Radioactive methods for determining geological age. *Rep. Progr. Phys.*, **19**, 80–103

Douglass, A. E., 1929: The secret of the southwest solved by talkative tree rings. *Nat. geogr. Mag.*, **56**, 737–770

Evernden, J. F., Curtis, G. H. and Kistler, R., 1957: Potassium–argon dating of Pleistocene volcanics. *Quaternaria*, **IV**, 13–17.

Faul, H. (Ed.), 1954: *Nuclear geology* (Ed. H. Faul), John Wiley, New York

Geer, G. de, 1940: Geochronologia sueccia principles. *K. svenska Vetensk. Akad. Handl.* (3) **18** (6), 360 pp., 90 pls

Jacobs, J. A., Russell, R. D. and Wilson, J. T., 1959: *Physics and Geology*, pp. 168–201

Kennedy, G. and Knopff, L., 1960: Dating by Thermoluminescence. *Archaeology*, **13**, 147–148

Lewis, D. R., Whitaker, T. N. and Chapman, C. W., 1959: Thermoluminescence of Rocks and Minerals. I—An apparatus for Quantitative Measurements. *Amer. Min.*, **44**, 1121–1140

Oakley, K. P., 1954: Analytic methods of dating bones. Report of British Association for the Advancement of Science Meeting at Oxford

Rankama, Kalervo, 1954: *Isotope Geology*, Pergamon Press, London

Russell, R. D. and Farquhar, R. M., 1960: *Lead Isotopes in Geology*, Interscience Publishers, New York and London

Specht, W. and Berg, S., 1959: Eine neue Technik als naturwissenschaftlicher Beitrag zur Datierung historischer und subfossiler Knochenfunde. *Technische Beiträge zur Archäologie, Mainz*, **1**, 81–103

Tilton, G. R. and Davis, G. L., 1959: Geochronology. *Researches in Geochemistry* (Ed. Abelson), pp. 190–216

Volchok, H. L. and Kulp, J. L., 1957: The ionium method of age determination. *Geochim. et cosmoch. Acta*, **11**, 219–246

Wright, H. E., 1957: The late-glacial chronology of Europe—a discussion. *Amer. J. Sci.*, **255**, 447–460

Zeller, E. J., 1954: Thermoluminescence in rocks. *Nuclear Geology* (Ed. H. Faul), John Wiley, New York, p. 180

Zeuner, F. E., 1958: *Dating the past*, 4th edn., Methuen, London

4+

CHAPTER 6

RADIOCARBON DATING

6.1 Introduction

When cosmic rays enter the earth's atmosphere neutrons are produced. These particles, being uncharged, are particularly effective in causing transmutations in the nucleus of any atom with which they collide. Such nuclear reactions have been extensively studied using artificially produced neutrons, and, from an appraisal of this data, Libby (1946) concluded that nearly all the cosmic-ray neutrons would end their lives by converting atmospheric nitrogen into a radioactive isotope of carbon, *carbon-14* or *radiocarbon* as it is alternatively called. Because its *chemical* behaviour is the same as that of ordinary carbon, it should form carbon dioxide molecules and mix in with the ordinary carbon dioxide of the atmosphere. Plant-life grows by photosynthesis of atmospheric carbon dioxide and in turn animals live off plants; consequently all the living animal and vegetable world (the *biosphere*) should be very weakly radioactive owing to the presence of a minute proportion of carbon-14 (approximately one atom of carbon-14 to a million million atoms of ordinary carbon). Atmospheric carbon dioxide also enters the oceans as dissolved carbonate, so this too should be weakly radioactive and any shells and deposits formed from it.

The same minute proportion of radiocarbon should also be present in human excreta, and confirmation of Libby's predictions was first obtained by measurements (Anderson, Libby, Weinhouse, Reid, Kirschenbaum and Grosse, 1947) on samples of the methane given off by City of Baltimore sewage! Subsequently the specific radioactivity of samples of living wood from widely different parts of the earth's surface was found to be uniform, and so too for samples of recently-formed sea shell (Libby, Anderson and Arnold, 1949).

All this was very satisfying confirmation of scientific theory; in addition Libby and his collaborators saw the possible application to age determination and included in their measurements samples of wood from the tombs of the Egyptian kings Zoser and

Sneferu. Radioactive atoms decay at a rate that is characteristic of the isotope and independent of all external conditions; for carbon-14 this rate is 1 per cent per 80 years, equivalent to a *half-life** of about 5600 years. In dead wood this loss of carbon-14 is not made up by fresh intake from the atmosphere and consequently the specific radioactivity of wood that has been dead for 5600 years should be half that of living wood. From historical records it was known that Zoser and Sneferu died within 75 years of 2700 B.C. and 2625 B.C. respectively, and consequently, assuming that the wood for the tombs was cut at about the same time, its specific radioactivity should be a little over half the value for living wood today. The expected value (averaged for the two tombs) was in fact 7·15 (± 0·15) counts per min per gram of carbon; the value measured experimentally by Libby, Anderson and Arnold was 7·04 (± 0·2) counts per min per gram, well within the limits of error and a powerful illustration of the archæological possibilities to be expected from radiocarbon dating.

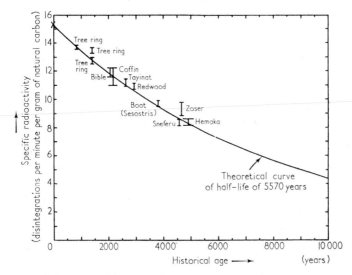

Fig. 6.1. Activity of samples of known age (after Libby, 1955). The uncertainty in historical age is indicated by the horizontal width of each mark; the statistical uncertainty in measurement is indicated by the vertical height. The solid curve represents the mathematical function 15·3 exp (− t/8033).

Further checks with samples of known age were then carried out (Arnold and Libby, 1949). The results (see Fig. 6.1) confirmed the validity, within the limits of error, of reversing the process and

---

* The period in which the number of radioactive atoms decreases to one half of the number present initially.

using the specific radiocarbon activity to obtain the age of un-known specimens, at any rate from 3000 B.C. forward. At first sight it might seem that, because the decay rate of radiocarbon is immutable, such checks are unnecessary. However, there is the fundamental assumption that the specific radiocarbon activity of the sample at death was the same as the activity of modern wood today. This will be true as long as the cosmic-ray intensity has remained constant on the one hand and the amount of normal carbon in the 'mixing reservoir' has stayed the same, on the other. The results shown in Fig. 6.1 cover the past 5000 years; there are no earlier historically-dated samples available but there is agree-ment (see, for example, Wright 1957) between radiocarbon dates and the chronology established by varve-counting (see Section 5.2) for the Late-Glacial period in Europe (ca. 9000 B.C.).

Thus the general validity of radiocarbon dating is firmly estab-lished. However, as more refined measuring techniques have been developed, a number of minor effects (e.g. the fossil-fuel effect, isotopic fractionation, delayed mixing) have been revealed, which, if not allowed for, can introduce errors of several hundred years. There is also evidence of a systematic uncertainty of at least ± 100 years (Vries, 1958) due to some as yet undetermined cause. Besides these general effects, in dating any individual sample there are the possibilities of sample contamination and of continued acquisi-tion of radiocarbon after death; there is also the uncertainty introduced by statistical fluctuations of radioactivity during measurement. Consequently the derivation of an accurate radiocarbon date calls for a highly critical appraisal of all factors.

Some archæologists, having initially accepted the method as an infallible panacea, tend to decry it as soon as small discrepancies arise. Both attitudes are undesirable because, as with all scientific methods, progress is only possible when there is critical co-opera-tion between the archæologist in the field and the scientist in the laboratory. There are many reasons why an individual radiocarbon date may be wrong (and even the simple possibility of fortuitous association between sample and archæological remains is some-times overlooked—for some ways in which this can happen see Tauber, 1958) but a series of carefully obtained dates for a given cultural phase, when considered in toto, provides reliable infor-mation of immense value unobtainable in any other way.

The method has been expounded by the originator, W. F. Libby, in his book Radiocarbon Dating, from which much of the informa-tion in the next section has been drawn.

6.2 General Principles

6.2.1 *Production of Neutrons by Cosmic Rays*

Fig. 6.2 shows the variation with height of the neutron intensity in the atmosphere, obtained from high altitude balloon measurements. The existence of a maximum in the region of 40 000 ft is evidence that the neutrons are *secondary* particles, produced within the earth's atmosphere by the primary cosmic rays. Apart from this, since an independent neutron is an unstable particle decaying with a half-life of 12 minutes into a proton, neutrons originating further away than the sun would not have time to reach the earth.

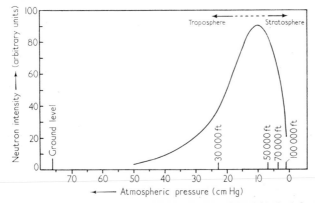

FIG. 6.2. Variation of cosmic-ray neutron intensity with altitude (after Libby, 1955). The measurements were made by balloon flights over New Jersey. There is considerable seasonal variation in the height of the troposphere.

Fig. 6.3 shows the variation with latitude of the neutron intensity at 30 000 ft. The explanation of the latitude variation assumes that the primary cosmic rays are electrically charged (this is another reason for believing the neutrons to be secondary), and consequently they are deflected by the magnetic field of the earth, unless they are travelling parallel to the lines of force. Consideration of Fig. 2.2 shows that particles approaching the earth in the polar regions will be deflected the least, and those approaching in the equatorial regions will be deflected the most. The ordinate scale in Fig. 6.3 is in fact the *geomagnetic* latitude, corresponding to the magnetic axis, which is displaced by up to 11° from the geographic latitude.

The measurements made by Libby, Anderson and Arnold (1949) showed that there is no latitude effect in the radiocarbon activity*

* More recent measurements show evidence of a slight latitude dependence (see § 6·4·7)

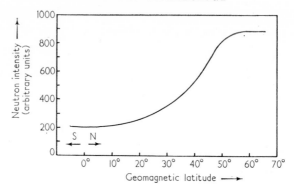

Fig. 6.3. Variation of cosmic-ray neutron intensity with latitude (after Libby, 1955). The measurements were made by balloon flights at 30 000 ft. Fortunately mixing within the atmosphere is sufficient to remove all traces of latitude dependence in the radiocarbon activity of terrestrial samples.

of samples of living wood. This indicates that thorough atmospheric mixing of radiocarbon occurs in a time short compared to the half-life of 5600 years, and consequently the latitude variation of radiocarbon production does not have to be considered.

As long as it has not changed with time, the actual value of the global neutron production rate is also unimportant. However, an estimate of it is valuable in determining whether there has been any large scale change and also in calculating the rate of mixing between various parts of the carbon 'exchange reservoir'. Various uncertainties, particularly in the energy spectrum of the neutrons themselves, make an accurate figure difficult to obtain; after reviewing the data available Craig (1957) suggests 6×10^{20} neutrons per min as the most likely figure, with an uncertainty of ± 25 per cent. This is equivalent to an average rate of $2 (\pm 0.5)$ neutrons per sec per sq cm of the earth's surface.

6.2.2   Production of Radiocarbon by Neutrons

Of the two major constituents of the atmosphere, oxygen is remarkably inert to neutron bombardment whereas for nitrogen the occurrence of a nuclear reaction is a thousand times more probable. With low-speed ('thermal') neutrons, the dominant reaction results in the production of carbon-14:

$$^{14}\mathrm{N} + n = {}^{14}\mathrm{C} + {}^{1}\mathrm{H} \qquad (6.1)$$

The *cross-section** for this reaction is about 1.7×10^{-24} cm².

---

* The cross-section represents the *effective* target area presented to a beam of neutrons by each nitrogen nucleus; any neutron scoring a hit produces the reaction to which the cross-section refers. It represents the probability of reaction rather than the actual physical size of the nucleus.

With fast-moving neutrons two additional reactions occur:

$$^{14}N + n = {}^{11}B + {}^{4}He \qquad (6.2)$$

$$^{14}N + n = {}^{12}C + {}^{3}H \qquad (6.3)$$

The cross-sections for these are very much smaller than for (6.1), except when comparing the effects of neutrons of high energy, and even then they are still small compared to the cross-section for (6.1) for thermal (low-energy) neutrons. Although the cosmic-ray neutrons probably have high energy on formation, they rapidly lose this energy by collisions and become thermal neutrons. Comparatively few neutrons reach the surface of the earth (see Fig. 6.2) and it is safe to assume that each neutron generated by cosmic rays produces a radiocarbon atom; consequently the neutron production rate equals the radiocarbon production rate. In terms of mass this amounts to 7·5 kilogram of radiocarbon per year.

Reaction (6.3) is not without interest. Tritium (^3H) is radioactive and decays, with a half-life of 12·5 years, to a stable, but rare, isotope of helium (^3He). This explains why the abundance of ^3He in atmospheric helium is ten times the average abundance in the earth's crust. Tritium itself has been detected in surface ocean water (Grosse, Johnston, Wolfgang and Libby, 1951) and it has been used (see Libby, 1959) as a 'natural tracer' in determining the rate at which deep ocean water (in which the tritium has decayed away) replaces surface water (in which the tritium is constantly replenished from the atmosphere). The tritium production rate by cosmic-ray neutrons is about 1 per cent of the radiocarbon production rate.

6.2.3 Radioactive Equilibrium

Because it is radioactive the amount of carbon-14 on earth does not increase indefinitely but remains at a constant level (assuming the rate of production to be constant). Carbon-14 decays back to nitrogen-14, at the same time emitting a beta particle (electron) with a maximum kinetic energy of 160 keV;

$$^{14}C = {}^{14}N + \beta^{-} \qquad (6.4)$$

This decay is a spontaneous process and the average rate at which it takes place is such that starting with a given (large) number of carbon-14 atoms approximately 1 per cent will have disintegrated after 80 years.

The equilibrium amount of carbon-14 on earth is simply obtained by equating this decay rate to the production rate (7·5 kilograms per year). Thus, if x kilograms is the equilibrium amount then

$$x \times \frac{1}{100} = 80 \times 7\cdot5 \qquad (6.5)$$

$$\therefore x = 60 \text{ metric tons}$$

6.2.4 *Distribution of Radiocarbon in Nature*

These 60 metric tons are somewhere on the earth. Fortunately, for the success of radiocarbon dating, they distribute themselves almost uniformly throughout the biosphere and the dissolved carbonate of the oceans. From Fig. 6.2 we see that most of the radiocarbon production takes place in the upper regions of the troposphere and the lower regions of the stratosphere. The carbon-14 atoms, chemically identical with ordinary carbon-12, are soon oxidized to carbon dioxide molecules. These then mix with the ordinary non-radioactive carbon dioxide of the atmosphere (0·046 per cent by weight) and except for the isotopic fractionation effect (see Section 6.4.5) the subsequent movements of the two types are indistinguishable—until, on the average after 8000 years, spontaneous decay of the carbon-14 nucleus takes place.

Carbon dioxide that is withdrawn from the atmosphere by plant-life is returned to it by the eventual decomposition that follows death. The same applies to carbon dioxide reaching the animal world *via* plant-life. Atmospheric carbon dioxide enters and leaves the oceans by means of an exchange reaction with the dissolved carbonate and bicarbonate ions; carbon reaches marine life (e.g. plankton) by photosynthesis and returns to the oceans by decomposition. A very small amount of carbon leaves the oceans by deposition as sedimentary rocks in the form of calcium carbonate; this loss is balanced by the carbon dioxide released into the atmosphere by weathering as the rocks become exposed. Except for the carbon locked up for long periods in rocks, the remainder forms the constituent parts of the 'exchange reservoir', between which the carbon atoms circulate fairly rapidly. To a first approximation this reservoir can be regarded as a giant tank throughout which the 60 metric tons of radiocarbon is distributed uniformly. The size of the tank is the 40 million million tons of carbon in the exchange reservoir (see Table 6.1), so that the ratio of carbon-14

Table 6.1. The carbon exchange reservoir (after Craig, 1957)

	Amount of carbon (million million tons)	Isotopic fractionation:[a] effect for carbon-14
Atmospheric carbon dioxide	0.64	1.037
Terrestrial biosphere (living)	0.3	1
Humus	1.10	1
Marine biosphere	0.01	1.024
Dissolved organic matter in sea	2.72	1.024
Total inorganic matter in sea	35.4	1.049
Total	40.2	

[a] See Section 6.4.5.

atoms to carbon-12 atoms is only 1 to 0.8 million million. In carbon that has been withdrawn from the reservoir, by death or deposition, the concentration of radiocarbon is of course lower still, decreasing exponentially, by 1 per cent every 80 years.

6.2.5   *Specific Radioactivity of Natural Carbon*

Such minute concentrations of radiocarbon are only detectable* by virtue of the beta rays emitted when the atoms decay according to equation (6.4). In 1 gram of natural carbon there are 5.02×10^{22} atoms of carbon and consequently 6.3×10^{10} atoms of carbon-14 if the sample was part of the exchange reservoir. Since 1 per cent of the carbon-14 atoms decay in 80 years, there will be 15 disintegrations per min per gram of natural carbon. This is also the rate of emission of beta particles, and it is equivalent to 6.75 *micro-microcuries†* per gram of natural carbon.

This figure for the specific radioactivity of natural carbon has been derived from the radiocarbon production rate, the size of the exchange reservoir, and the decay rate of radiocarbon. Bearing in mind the 25 per cent uncertainty in the production rate we cannot expect too good an agreement between this derived value and values measured experimentally. However, for wood the latter (Suess, 1955) is 14.7 ($\pm$ 0.4) disintegrations per min per gram. This indicates that there have been no violent changes in the production rate or the reservoir size during the past 8000 years

* In principle a *mass spectrometer* could be used but for such a small mass difference the concentrations involved are well below the lower limit of sensitivity of this instrument.

† The *curie* is the unit normally used for expressing the strength of a radioactive source. It is equivalent to 3.7×10^{10} disintegrations per second.

4*

(the average life-time of a carbon-14 atom); if such changes had occurred then the present-day radiocarbon concentration would not have yet reached equilibrium with the present-day production rate (or reservoir size).

6.2.6   Radioactive Decay

In mathematical terms, the decay rate of a radioactive isotope is *exponential*. Let us define τ, in years, such that $(1/\tau)$ is the fraction of a given sample of carbon-14 atoms that decay per year (so that the decay rate of 1 per cent per 80 years is equivalent to $\tau = 8000$ years). This may be expressed by the differential equation

$$-\left(\frac{\mathrm{d}N}{\mathrm{d}t}\right) = \frac{1}{\tau} \times N \qquad (6.6)$$

where N is the number of carbon-14 atoms present in the sample at any instant. The solution of equation (6.6), obtained by integration, is

$$N = N_0 \exp\left(-t/\tau\right) \qquad (6.7)$$

where N_0 is the initial number of atoms (at $t = 0$). The value of $\exp\left(-t/\tau\right)$ for any value of t is obtained from mathematical tables. Its form is illustrated by the solid curve in Fig. 6.1.

It is usual to state the decay rate in terms of the half-life, T. This is the value of t for which $N = \frac{1}{2}N_0$. Since $\exp\left(-t/\tau\right) = 0.5$ for $(t/\tau) = 0.693$, it follows that $T = 0.693\tau$. Experimentally the value of $(1/\tau)$ is found from measurements on artificially-produced carbon-14, and the accepted value of T deduced from these is 5568 ($\pm$ 30) years, corresponding to a best value for τ of 8033 years. It can be shown that this is also the average life of a carbon-14 atom. The average life is the more appropriate duration to have in mind when considering up to how long ago past changes in the cosmic-ray intensity would affect present-day conditions, but the half-life is more convenient in calculating the radioactivity of 'dead' carbon. Thus:

after   5570 years (T) $N = \frac{1}{2}N_0$
after 11140 years $(2T)$ $N = \frac{1}{4}N_0$
after 16710 years $(3T)$ $N = \frac{1}{8}N_0$
after 22280 years $(4T)$ $N = \frac{1}{16}N_0$

. . . .
after 66840 years $(12T)$ $N = \frac{1}{4096}N_0$
etc.

We have seen that the specific radioactivity of 'live' carbon is about 15 disintegrations per min per gram of carbon. After

22 000 years this will be down by a factor of 16 to about 1 disintegration per min per gram. But for carbon that has been dead for three times as long, i.e. 66 000 years, the disintegration rate is very small indeed and can only be measured by the use of special techniques (isotopic enrichment, see Section 6.5.6).

The necessity of avoiding contaminating a sample of old carbon with modern carbon becomes more and more important as the age increases. Thus the addition of 1 per cent of modern carbon to a sample that is 5570 years old, increases the specific radioactivity by 2 per cent, so that the measured age of the sample is too small by 160 years, an error of 3 per cent. For a sample that is 23 000 years old, the addition of 1 per cent of modern carbon increases the specific radioactivity by 16 per cent, corresponding to 1300 years, an error of 5 per cent. But for a sample that is 67 000 years old, the addition of 1 per cent of modern carbon makes the radioactivity 40 times what it should be. The indicated age would be 37 000 years; this bears no relation to the true age and depends only on the degree of contamination. The effect of sample contamination is illustrated in Fig. 6.4.

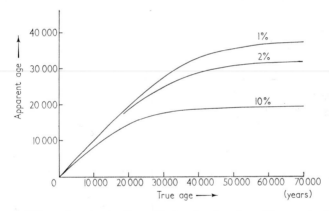

Fig. 6.4. Effect of contamination with 'modern' carbon. The curves show the apparent radiocarbon age obtained due to the inadvertent addition of 1 per cent, 2 per cent, and 10 per cent of carbon derived from living organic matter.

6.2.7 *Statistical Fluctuations*

Because radioactive decay is a spontaneous process, the observed rates of disintegration will vary about the average values. The probability that a particular carbon-14 atom will disintegrate within 80 years is 1 in 100, and clearly the term 'decay rate' has no meaning in this case. But if a million carbon-14 atoms are considered, the combined probabilities give a more or less steady decay rate. Statistical considerations show that if the true average rate is x disintegrations per min and the measurement time is t min, then there is a 68 per cent probability that the observed number of disintegrations will lie within $\sqrt{(xt)}$ of the true number, xt. Expressed in percentage, these limits of error correspond to

$$\pm \frac{100}{\sqrt{(xt)}} \%$$

The quantity $\sqrt{(xt)}$ is called the *standard deviation* (s. d.). The probability that the observed number lies within *two* standard deviations of the true number is 95·5 per cent, and within three standard deviations, 99·7 per cent.

The percentage error decreases as the square root of the observation time but, as we shall see shortly, the counting rates obtained in practice necessitate measurement for at least 24 hours in order to reduce the standard deviation to several per cent. To reduce this by a further factor of 10 requires an increase in the measurement time by a factor of 100, and not many samples get measured if that is done·

It cannot be too strongly emphasized that the limits of error quoted with the age deduced for a specimen represent the standard deviation, i.e. the limits within which there is a 68 per cent probability that the true age lies. There are *no* limits within which the true age lies with absolute certainty.

6.2.8   *Effect of Counter Background*

For old samples statistical fluctuations in the counter 'background' become the dominant limitation. This background arises mainly from cosmic rays which penetrate through to the counter despite the various shielding precautions (see Section 6.5.3); the background counting rate in most installations amounts to at least 10 per cent of the counting rate for modern carbon. Although the average background rate can be determined accurately by counting over a long period, this does nothing to reduce the statistical fluctuations in the background that may occur while the sample itself is being measured; while simultaneous background measurement in a second counter placed close by is a valuable check on a systematic change during the sample count (e.g. due to sun-spot activity, or fall-out from bomb tests), the statistical fluctuations in the two counters are independent.

Suppose the average background for a certain counter is B counts per min and the measured counting rate averaged over t min for a given sample is S counts/min. Then the standard deviations are $\sqrt{(Bt)}$ and $\sqrt{(St)}$ respectively. The standard deviation on the net sample count $(St - Bt)$ is the square root of the *sum* of the squares of the individual standard deviations, i.e. $\sqrt{(B+S)t}$. If B is 10 per cent of $(S - B)$ for modern carbon, for carbon that is say 20 000 years old, the standard deviation will exceed the net sample count unless t is made long. Measurement time is usually 24 hours, i.e. $t = 1440$ min; in this case the ratio of net sample count to standard deviation equals

$$\frac{S - B}{\sqrt{(S + B)}} \times 38$$

The limiting meaningful age that can be reached is usually taken as that for which $(St - Bt)$ is four times $\sqrt{(St)}$.

It is useful to define a figure of merit Q, where

$$Q = \frac{S_0 - B}{\sqrt{B}}$$

S_0 being the counting rate for modern carbon. For a good installation Q may reach 25, but lower values (~ 10) are more usual. For a counting time of 24 hours, and denoting the limiting age counting rate by S_L, we have

$$\frac{S_L - B}{S_0 - B} = \frac{0 \cdot 1}{Q}$$

assuming $S_L \approx B$, a good approximation for samples older than 20 000 years. Substituting $Q = 13$,

$$\frac{S_L - B}{S_0 - B} = \frac{1}{128}$$

which corresponds (see Section 6.2.6) to a limiting age of seven half-lives, i.e. 39 000 years. For $Q = 7$, the corresponding age is 33 000 years, and 45 000 years for $Q = 26$. To reach 70 000 years would require $Q \sim 600$.

6.3 Suitability of Sample

The most important question is whether or not any exchange of carbon has occurred since death—the presumed time of removal of the sample from the exchange reservoir. Such exchange is least likely when the molecular structure is large. In addition, the sample should be in a well-preserved condition since decomposition may represent the assimilation of fresh carbon. Charcoal and well-preserved wood are accepted as the best type of sample;

exchange is unlikely and the only decomposition conceivable is the evolution of carbon monoxide or dioxide. This does not matter since it represents removal only. As with all samples, intrusive rootlets and fibres must be carefully removed and any deposited carbonates dissolved out by treatment with acid. Alkali washing can be used to remove humic matter.

Well-preserved wood is highly reliable because it consists largely of big cellulose molecules; the reliability of wood is well-confirmed by radiocarbon dating of inner tree-rings—the radioactivity of each ring corresponds to the date of *formation* despite the presence of carbon of higher and lower radioactivity in adjacent rings on either side. Thus the possibility must be borne in mind that samples of wood and charcoal were derived from the inner rings of a slow-growing tree (such as oak or redwood) in which case the radiocarbon date can be several hundred years older than the archæological event of felling the tree.

Peat, leaves, nuts, hair, skin, and leather are fairly reliable as long as great care is taken to remove all intrusive material. With peat there is the possibility of absorption by the sample of humic acids which have seeped down from above but these can be removed by chemical purification. Another possible source of error (Deevey *et al.*, 1954) is that the sample material was derived from submerged plants in hard water, which grew by photosynthesis of dissolved bicarbonate; such carbon originates from the limestone through which the water has passed and is 'old'.

Paper, cloth, dentine, charred bone and antler can also be dated. Bone and antler which are uncharred are of doubtful reliability, except in specially favourable circumstances; in addition the carbon content is low (less than 10 per cent for air-dried bone). Antler is better than bone because of its hairy structure. The porous nature of bone facilitates the deposition of extraneous carbonates but even after the removal of the inorganic part by acid treatment and of the absorbed humic acids by alkali washing, the results obtained from the remaining organic material (mainly protein) can be inconsistent (e.g. Münnich, 1957).

The carbon-14 content of sea shell is a reliable measure of its age as long as it is coarse-grained. Fine-grained, recrystallized shell is not reliable. In particular with shell it is necessary to take account of *isotopic fractionation* (see also Section 6.4.5). In the exchange of carbon dioxide between atmosphere and ocean, there is preferential uptake of carbon-14 by the ocean which, if other factors did not intervene, would result in the carbon-14 concentration being just over 1 per cent higher than in the atmosphere.

There is a similar, but reverse, fractionation between the atmosphere and plant-life, the effect amounting to nearly 4 per cent. For the most precise work it is desirable to evaluate the fractionation effect for each sample measured; this can be done by finding the degree of fractionation between carbon-13 and carbon-12 in the sample. Carbon-13, being stable, is unaffected by age considerations and its concentration gives a true evaluation of the fractionation effect. The effect for carbon-14 is twice as great. The carbon-13 to carbon-12 ratio is about 1:100 and the exact ratio in the sample can be accurately measured by means of a mass spectrometer and compared with the ratio for a standard sample. Such additional measurements are only necessary when dealing with fairly recent samples in which errors of a few hundred years are important (an error of 80 years is introduced by uncorrected fractionation of 1 per cent).

The amount of sample necessary for a measurement varies both with the type of sample and with the measuring installation. Table 6.2 shows the amounts suggested by Broecker and Kulp (1956), assuming a typical gas proportional system.

Table 6.2. Necessary amounts of different sample types
(after Broecker and Kulp, 1956)

Sample type	Optimum amount (grams)	Minimum amount (grams)
Calcium carbonate	120	4
Carbon	10	0·4
Wood	50	1
Charcoal	40	1
Peat	100	2
Shell	180	8
Bone (charred)	100	2
Bone (uncharred)	1200	50

6.4 Complications

The basic idea of radiocarbon dating is simple enough. It rests on three fundamental assumptions: firstly, that the radiocarbon concentration is the same in all parts of the exchange reservoir; secondly, that this concentration has not changed with time; and thirdly, that the half-life of carbon-14 is 5568 ($\pm$ 30) years. There is no question of any fluctuation in the half-life but, if the accepted value is in error by a certain percentage then there will be a systematic error of the same percentage in all radiocarbon ages. The value of 5568 years is the weighted mean (Libby, 1955, p. 36) of three independent measurements of the disintegration rate, made in 1949; a new measurement of this important constant is nearing completion at the National Bureau of Standards.

We now proceed to discuss effects which cause, or could cause, deviations from the first two basic assumptions. These may be classified as follows:

(a) Variations in the carbon-14 production rate.

(b) Variations in the size of the exchange reservoir.

(c) Finite mixing rates between different parts of the reservoir (as against the assumption of instantaneous mixing).

(d) Isotopic fractionation, i.e. preferential take-up of carbon-14 relative to carbon-12, by some parts of the reservoir.

Definite evidence about (a) and (b) is difficult to obtain except from measurements on samples reliably dated by other means, and it is, of course, outside the periods covered by other dating systems that the need for carbon dating is greatest. Apart from the possibility of past variations under (a) and (b) there are two recent effects (production by H-bomb tests, and dilution by fossil-fuel combustion) that have certainly changed the present-day radiocarbon concentration: these necessitate the use of reference samples, usually tree-rings, prior to the industrial revolution, in order to arrive at the correct value for the radiocarbon activity of the exchange reservoir—an accurate value is vital since all ages are deduced from the ratio of the sample activity to the exchange reservoir activity.

Correction for isotopic fractionation (d) can be made by measurement of the $^{13}C/^{12}C$ ratio in the sample as already mentioned. Although present-day mixing rates (c) can be established by measurement (after allowance for the H-bomb and fossil-fuel effects) and their effect on dating evaluated, it is possible that there have been fluctuations in these rates in the past, giving rise to a small residual uncertainty in all radiocarbon dates (see Section 6.4.7).

6.4.1 Constancy of Cosmic-Ray Intensity

Although a cosmic phenomenon would not be expected to vary except on a cosmic time-scale, the actual intensity of the cosmic radiation which reaches the upper atmosphere is affected firstly by the magnetic field of the earth, and secondly by interplanetary magnetic fields generated by electric currents in the sun's corona (Elliot, 1960). Short term cosmic ray fluctuations due to the latter effect have been observed and these correlate with sun-spot activity; there is as yet no direct evidence whether or not changes due to this cause can persist long enough to affect the radiocarbon equilibrium appreciably (but see Section 6.4.7).

The effect on cosmic radiation of the magnetic field of the earth itself has been known for some time. In equatorial regions the minimum energy of cosmic particles is greater than in high latitudes; this arises from the deflection away from the earth of charged particles that are travelling perpendicular to the lines of force of the earth's field (see Fig. 2.2). The latitude dependence of cosmic-ray neutron production results from this (see Fig. 6.3) but it need not be taken into consideration because of efficient atmospheric mixing. However, if at any time in the past the magnetic field of the earth had been *higher* than at present, the shielding effect would have been greater and the overall radiocarbon production rate *lower*. This in turn would cause radiocarbon ages to be *older* than the true age.

There is evidence from the intensity of thermo-remanent magnetism found in baked clay (see Section 7.7.2) that, 2000 years ago, in France, the earth's magnetic field strength was nearly twice its present-day value. Although it seems likely, it still needs to be established that this was a world-wide effect. Assuming that it was so, Elsasser, Ney and Winckler (1956) have estimated the consequent radiocarbon dating error on two hypotheses as to the time variation of the effect:

(*i*) If the magnetic field intensity had been constant up to 2000 years ago, thereafter following an exponential decrease to its present-day value, the radiocarbon age deduced (ignoring the effect) for a sample of true age 2000 years, would be 2240 years.

(*ii*) If the exponential fall has continued since 4000 years ago, the field being constant before that, then the radiocarbon age obtained for a sample of true age 4000 years would be 5000 years.

On the other hand, if the thermo-remanent results represent a fluctuation lasting over a period appreciably shorter than the mean life of radiocarbon (8000 years) then the effects will be much smaller. The amount of radiocarbon on the earth is an equilibrium value determined, loosely speaking, by the *average* production rate over the past 8000 years. There are four arguments against any gross, long-term variation in the radiocarbon production rate:

(*i*) The ages for samples back to 5000 years ago are in reasonable agreement with historical estimates (Arnold and Libby, 1949; Ralph and Stuckenrath 1960).

(*ii*) Radiocarbon dates for the beginning of the Post-Glacial period (about 10 000 years ago) in N. W. Europe agree with the varve chronology. Similarly for the Boreal–Atlantic change of forest-type (about 8000 years ago).

(*iii*) Radiocarbon dating of some deep-sea mud samples by Kulp and Volchok (1953) agreed with the date established by another radioactive age method (ionium) which is independent of the cosmic-ray intensity. The precision obtained was poor but limited the possible change in the radiocarbon production rate to less than $\pm$ 10–20 per cent over the past 35 000 years.

(*iv*) The calculated value for the radiocarbon activity of the exchange reservoir, on the assumption that the cosmic-ray intensity has been at its present-day value for the past 8000 years or so, is in reasonable agreement with that found experimentally (see Section 6.2.5).

These arguments certainly do not exclude the possibility of small systematic errors of several hundred years. Indeed, the few known-age samples in the period 1000 B.C. to 3000 B.C., that have been measured more precisely than by Libby and Arnold (1949), show a radiocarbon age that is consistently too young, according to Egyptian chronology, by between 200 and 400 years (Vries, Barendsen, and Waterbolk, 1958; Vries and Waterbolk, 1958; Ralph and Stuckenrath, 1960). This may be the fault of the Egyptian chronology, or because the accepted half-life is too low, or it may truly represent one of the complicating effects discussed in this section. However, it is to be noted that the discrepancy is in the opposite direction to that implied by the magnetic intensity results; in addition there is little support for the prediction that the age of 2000 year-old samples will be overestimated.

6.4.2   *Variation in Size of Exchange Reservoir*

The foregoing arguments assume that the reservoir size has remained constant, so that they are evidence for this too, unless changes in production rate and in reservoir size have mutually compensated. If magnetic measurements, when extended further back in time, indicate a long-term reduction in the production rate then this will imply a compensating decrease in reservoir size. From Table 6.1 we see that the ocean carbonate forms the bulk of the reservoir. Libby (1955, p. 31) has pointed out that the lowering of the sea-level during the last Ice Age by about 100 metres represents a decrease of about 5 per cent in the reservoir size. The effect might be further enhanced by a reduction in the concentration of dissolved carbonate due to reduced ocean temperature, and Libby considers that the overall reduction might amount to 10 per cent. This would make the radiocarbon dates for glacial material too young by 800 years—unless compensated by a decrease in the production rate.

6.4.3   The Fossil-Fuel Effect (or 'Suess' Effect)

The combustion of coal and oil releases into the atmosphere large quantities of carbon dioxide from which the carbon-14 has long disappeared, because the coal and oil were removed from the exchange reservoir millions of years ago. This 'old' carbon dilutes the carbon-14 concentration in the atmosphere and the activity of wood samples, grown say in 1950 (prior to H-bomb tests), is in fact lower than samples grown in 1850 (prior to the industrial revolution), despite the decay that has occurred in the latter. The effect was first established by Suess (1955). It has also been found that the activity of atmospheric carbon dioxide is lower in the neighbourhood of large cities than elsewhere.

It is estimated that the old carbon released in this way from 1860 to 1954 amounts to 13 per cent of the existing carbon content of the atmosphere, or 0·2 per cent of the carbon in the whole exchange reservoir. If mixing into the whole reservoir was instantaneous the dilution effect would be too small to be detectable. In fact the radiocarbon activity of samples grown in 1954 is approximately 2 per cent lower than the activity calculated from measurements on pre-1850 tree-rings after allowing for radioactive decay. Fergusson (1958) has deduced from these figures that the average time spent by a carbon dioxide molecule in the atmosphere before entry into other parts of the reservoir is probably about 2 years, and certainly not greater than 7 years. These figures may be too low because of partial compensation of the fossil-fuel effect by the short-term fluctuations discussed in Section 6.4.7.

The importance of the fossil-fuel effect was realized only after many dating laboratories had established the use of a recently grown sample as a measure of the exchange activity in the past. As a result the ages published by some laboratories are too young by 100–200 years. The error varies from laboratory to laboratory as there are other factors involved too. The position is now being regularized by the distribution of two international carbon-14 standards: oxalic acid by the National Bureau of Standards, and samples of sodium carbonate by Heidelberg University. These standards are being used to recalibrate the individual counting installations so that precise comparison of results will now be possible.

6.4.4 *Carbon-14 Production by H-bomb Tests*

It has been estimated that bomb explosions up to July 1959 have produced about half a ton of carbon-14. If this were distributed throughout the exchange reservoir uniformly, the radiocarbon activity would only be a little under one per cent higher than in the pre-bomb era. However, as with the fossil-fuel effect, delay in mixing gives rise to a more striking change temporarily. The radiocarbon activity of recently grown plants has risen continuously since 1954 reaching 25 per cent above normal by 1959. The continued rise after the cessation of H-bomb tests in 1958 is attributed to delay in descent from the stratosphere. Broecker and Olson (1960) have estimated that the bomb excess in the troposphere will reach a maximum of 30 to 40 per cent sometime before 1963, and that by 1980 the excess will have decreased to half its maximum value. As with the fossil-fuel effect, the observed excesses in different parts of the reservoir can be used to derive mixing-rates.

6.4.5 *Isotopic Fractionation*

Although carbon-14 is identical to carbon-12 in its chemical behaviour, its higher atomic weight does manifest itself in nature. The mechanism of the exchange reaction between atmospheric carbon dioxide and ocean carbonate, favours a slightly higher (by 1·2 per cent) carbon-14 concentration in the ocean carbonate; conversely the photosynthesis of atmospheric carbon dioxide into terrestrial plant-life results in a slightly lower (by 3·7 per cent on the average) carbon-14 concentration in the latter. The figures quoted have been evaluated by Craig (1954), using as data the enrichment factors found for carbon-13 by mass spectrometer measurements; the effects for carbon-14 are obtained by doubling the percentage enrichments found for carbon-13.

6.4.6 *Mixing within the Reservoir—Apparent Age of Ocean Carbonate*

Because the carbon-13 concentration in ocean carbonate is about 2·5 per cent higher than in wood we expect the carbon-14 concentration to be higher by 5 per cent. In fact, the initial activity of pre-industrial revolution tree-rings (obtained by correcting the activity measured today for radioactive decay—1 per cent per 80 years) is the same as that of ocean carbonate (Suess, 1955), i.e. the activity of ocean carbonate is 5 per cent lower than we expected. This can be expressed alternatively by saying that ocean carbonate has an *apparent age* of 400 years.* This apparent age arises because freshly produced carbon-14 atoms are not distributed throughout the exchange reservoir instantaneously. The existence of a finite delay in mixing has already been inferred from the magnitude of the fossil-fuel effect which would be negligible if instantaneous mixing took place. It would be surprising if it did, having regard to the vast bulk of material concerned.

The way in which mixing rates can be evaluated is illustrated by the following simplified calculation. Let the mixing rate between carbon dioxide in the atmosphere and ocean carbonate be x per cent per year of all the carbon-12 in the atmosphere. This means that $(x/100)V_a$ carbon-12 atoms enter the ocean each year, V_a being the number of carbon-12 atoms in the atmosphere; this must be balanced by the entry of the same amount into the atmosphere from the ocean. Now in the absence† of fractionation effects the carbon leaving the ocean would be 5 per cent lower in carbon-14 concentration than that leaving the atmosphere. Therefore if R is the carbon-14/carbon-12 concentration in the atmosphere, the yearly flow of carbon-14 from ocean to atmosphere equals $0.95\ R(x/100)V_a$ and from atmosphere to ocean equals $1.00\ R(x/100)V_a$. The net yearly transport of carbon-14 from atmosphere to ocean will be

$$\frac{0.05x}{100}\,(RV_a)$$

i.e. $0.05x$ per cent of the carbon-14 in the atmosphere.

At equilibrium the yearly production rate is $(1/8033) \times$ (total amount of carbon-14 on earth). From Table 6.1, and since the

---

* An error of ± 100 years should be associated with this owing to imprecision in the data used. There is also the possibility that the apparent age has been increased artificially by a slight fossil-fuel effect having now reached the sea. This effect is unlikely to exceed 1 per cent and is therefore within the error quoted (Craig, 1957).

† The argument still holds in the actual situation (if fossil-fuel effects are allowed for) but is a little more complicated. Owing to fractionation the carbon-14 concentration in the atmosphere is 3.7 per cent higher than in wood. The concentration in wood is experimentally found to be the same as in ocean carbonate. Therefore the flow from atmosphere to ocean will be 3.7 per cent higher than in the reverse direction. Fractionation between atmosphere and ocean enhances this by a further 1.2 per cent, making 4.9 per cent in all.

carbon-14 concentration is *approximately* uniform throughout the reservoir:

$$\frac{\text{Carbon-14 in atmosphere}}{\text{Total carbon-14 in reservoir}} = \frac{0.64}{40.2} = \frac{1}{62.7}$$

Consequently, since nearly all the carbon-14 produced reaches the ocean,

$$\frac{0.05x}{100}(RV_a) = \left(\frac{1}{8033}\right) \times 62.7 \times (RV_a)$$

$\therefore x = 15.6$ per cent per year.

An alternative way of expressing this is to say that the average *residence time* of a carbon atom in the atmosphere before absorption in the ocean is $(100/15.6) = 6.4$ years.

A full treatment of mixing rates has been given by Craig (1957) and the preferred estimates deduced by him are shown in Fig. 6.5.

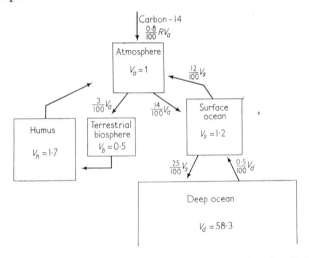

Fig. 6.5. Mixing-rates within the carbon exchange reservoir (after Craig, 1957). V_a, V_b, etc. indicate the size of each compartment relative to $V_a = 1$. Arrows indicate the yearly transfer of carbon-12 in terms of the appropriate compartment size, except for the arrow at the top which shows the yearly production of carbon-14 by cosmic-ray neutrons in terms of (RV_a), the equilibrium amount of carbon-14 in the atmosphere.

The exchange reservoir has been divided into five compartments: atmosphere, surface ocean (the layer above the thermocline, about 50–100 metres deep), deep ocean, terrestrial biosphere and humus. Except in the last, instantaneous mixing is assumed within each compartment. Although the apparent age of carbon in the surface ocean is 400 years, the average residence time in the deep ocean, according to this model, is $(100/0.5) = 200$ years. This is not contradictory for the carbon in the surface layer is a mixture of 'reinvigorated' carbon from the atmosphere and 'old' carbon from the deep ocean. The latter will have an apparent age of 400 years plus the residence time, i.e. 600 years. The apparent age exceeds the residence time because of continued circulation.

6.4.7 Short-term Fluctuations

Precise measurements by Vries (1958) on dated tree-rings of the past 500 years have established the existence of short-term variations in reservoir activity. Fig. 6.6 shows the initial activity for

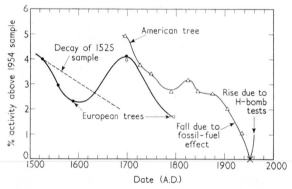

FIG. 6.6. Fluctuations in the initial activity of dated samples (after Vries, 1958). The samples used were tree-rings so that their date of removal from the reservoir could be found precisely by counting. The initial activity is calculated by correcting for the radioactivity since the ring was formed (1 per cent for each 80 years). More recent measurements show that the H-bomb rise reached 25 per cent in 1959.

these samples after correction for radioactive decay. Subsequent work (Willis, Tauber and Münnich, 1960) has extended these measurements back to 1300 years ago with similar results; the maximum fluctuation from the mean is about 1·5 per cent giving rise to a dating uncertainty of ± 120 years. This excludes the fossil-fuel effect which is evident in Fig. 6.6 after 1850.

Two reasons for these fluctuations have been suggested (Vries, 1958 and 1959): variations in mixing rates and variations in cosmic-ray intensity due to sun-spot activity. Although changes must persist for the order of 8000 years to have an appreciable effect on the radiocarbon equilibrium concentration, short-term changes can produce minor fluctuations. This is because the atmosphere and biosphere are, to a slight degree, isolated from the major part of the reservoir—the oceans. Thus if the radiocarbon production rate suddenly increased by 25 per cent, while no change would occur in the ocean for several hundred years, the radiocarbon concentration of the atmosphere and biosphere would increase to a new equilibrium level, higher by 2 per cent, within 10 years or so. Some recent high altitude neutron intensity measurements suggest that such violent short-term changes can in fact occur* (Vries, 1959).

There is correlation between the fluctuations of Fig. 6.6 and the records of sun-spot activity. There is also correlation with records of glacier advance and retreat, which are an indication of the general level of the earth's temperature. This fits the explanation in terms of mixing-rate fluctuations—Vries suggests that a change in temperature would alter the mixing rate between surface ocean and deep ocean. An increase by 50 per cent would reduce the atmospheric radiocarbon concentration by 2 per cent. Increased oceanic mixing can be envisaged as the arrival at the surface of deep water which is low in radiocarbon activity after a long period of submersion.

Whatever the explanation it is clear that there is a definite limit (of at least ± 100 years) to the accuracy that can be claimed for radiocarbon dates quite apart from statistical fluctuations. Even calibration of the reservoir activity does not overcome this, for since the rate of change of activity is greater than 1 per cent in 80 years over certain portions of the curve in Fig. 6.6, it is possible for two samples, say of dates 1525 and 1625, to have identical activities today. Furthermore there appears to be a 1 per cent difference between the activities of the tree samples from America and from Europe, suggesting the possibility of geographical variations. Latitudinal differences have also been noted in the H-bomb rise and it has been suggested (Tauber, 1960) that the same mechanism is responsible for both effects and also for the short-term fluctuations. All this emphasizes that the most valuable rôle of radiocarbon dating is in prehistory where such small effects do not matter.

6.5 Measuring the Radioactivity

Accurate measurement is difficult and tedious for several reasons. Because the degree of radioactivity is very low, each measurement must continue for a long time in order to average

---

* The acceptance of such large changes in the radiocarbon production rate makes it difficult to explain the agreement between the measured production rate and the observed present-day radiocarbon concentration (see Section 6.2.5), except as a remarkable coincidence.

out statistical fluctuations. Stringent precautions must be taken in the construction of the measuring equipment to use materials completely free from radioactive contamination. The equipment must be shielded from cosmic rays—otherwise the effect of the sample itself will be negligible. Besides being weak in terms of number of disintegrations per minute, the beta rays emitted are weak in terms of penetrating power; the intensity is roughly halved by a 1-in. thickness of air, or by a 0·0003-in. thickness of aluminium. Consequently the sample must be inserted inside the Geiger counter (or proportional counter) itself in order that the beta rays reach the sensitive volume.

6.5.1 *The Solid Carbon Method*

The measuring instrument originated by Libby was the *screen-wall* counter. The sample was obtained as solid carbon by chemical treatment and painted onto the inner surface of the cylinder of a specially constructed Geiger counter. This technique has now been discontinued because the painting process necessitated exposure of the highly absorptive carbon to the atmosphere and subsequent to the hydrogen-bomb tests of 1954 this involved risk of radioactive contamination. Another disadvantage of the method was the low efficiency: only 5 per cent of the disintegrations in the sample register in the Geiger counter. The sample size required was 8 grams of carbon—unpleasantly large in many archæological circumstances.

The solid carbon technique and the associated sample preparation have been fully described by Libby (1955).

6.5.2 *Gas Proportional Counters*

The low efficiency of the solid carbon method arises from absorption of beta particles in the carbon layer itself. This can be avoided by converting the carbon into a gas—carbon dioxide (CO_2), acetylene (C_2H_2) and methane (CH_4) have all proved satisfactory—and using it as the counting-gas of a *proportional* counter. Although the electrical pulses from a proportional counter are much smaller than from a Geiger counter there is the advantage that the size is *proportional* to the energy of the beta particle initiating each pulse. The beta particles from carbon-14 have energies spreading from zero up to 160 keV, so by using an electronic pulse analyser to reject pulses corresponding to a beta-particle energy of greater than 160 keV it is possible to discriminate against interfering high-energy background (e.g. due to alpha contamination).

Carbon dioxide is the most commonly used gas despite the parti-cular care that must be taken in its preparation to eliminate electronegative impurities which would make it useless as a counter gas. Acetylene has the disadvantage of explosion-risk. The volume of the counter is in most cases several litres and this is filled with the appropriate gas at a pressure of one or two atmos-pheres; the sample size is of the order of 1 or 2 grams of carbon—much less than in the solid carbon method—and allowing for some 'dead volume' the counting rate obtained from a contemporary sample is usually about 10–20 counts/min.

In preparation of the counter gas the first step is to convert the sample into carbon dioxide: by combustion for an organic sample, by treatment with acid for carbonate samples. After various stages of purification, the sample is obtained in convenient form, as barium carbonate or lithium carbide for example. Immediately prior to measurement, the gas is evolved chemically (e.g. addition of orthophosphoric acid to barium carbonate to obtain carbon dioxide, addition of water to lithium carbide to obtain acetylene). Subsequent to measurement the sample is kept for future reference. For details of the various chemical systems that have been employ-ed the reader should consult the original papers; e.g. for carbon dioxide, Vries and Barendson (1953), Godwin, Walker and Willis (1957); for acetylene, Suess (1954); for methane, Burke and Meinshein (1955). An important consideration in all methods is the yield: that is, the percentage of the carbon in the original sample which is converted into gaseous form. It is desirable that this should be 100 per cent so as to avoid any possibility that the carbon-14 has been preferentially converted with respect to the carbon-12, or *vice-versa*.

6.5.3 *Shielding and Background Reduction*

Without shielding the cosmic-ray background would swamp even the 'modern' carbon counting rate, and background reduction is one of the major problems in designing an installation. The gamma-ray component is usually removed by surrounding the counter with a screen of steel, at least 8 in. thick. Massive though it is, this does not stop the highly penetrating meson com-ponent of the cosmic rays. The mesons are eliminated by means of an *anti-coincidence shield*; this consists of a ring of Geiger counters placed around the measuring counter inside the iron screen. Any meson that reaches the measuring counter should have also pro-duced a pulse in one of the Geiger counters and it is arranged electronically that a pulse from the measuring counter occurring

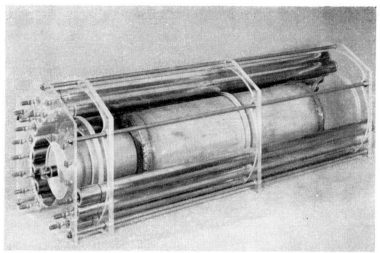

(*By kind permission of HMSO, National Physical Laboratory*)

PLATE XIX. Radiocarbon dating—the counter. The proportional counter itself is in the centre. The thin tubes surrounding it (some have been removed for clarity) are the anti-coincidence Geiger counters.

(*By kind permission of HMSO, National Physical Laboratory*)

PLATE XX. Radiocarbon dating—shielding against cosmic-ray background. Provision is made for several counters; sliding doors complete the screen.

simultaneously is disregarded. The reduction in background effected by the steel screen depends very much on the situation of the counter, e.g. the amount of constructional material in the laboratory building (it goes without saying that the installation should not be near to other radioisotope work). The anti-coincidence shield, if efficient, achieves a further reduction by a factor of the order of 100.

Some additional attenuation of the background can be obtained by means of a screen of paraffin wax impregnated with boric acid. This absorbs neutrons generated by cosmic rays in the steel screen itself.

The need for use of materials free from residual radioactivity has already been mentioned, particularly in the construction of the counter and the anti-coincidence shield. This is often a matter of trial and error (and the error can be very expensive) but, in general for the counter, stainless steel, electrolytic copper, and quartz are preferred materials. Glass can only be used if free from potassium (which has a weak natural radioactivity). Lead, the standard shielding material, is well-known for its natural radioactivity and unless specially selected can only be used as a preliminary *outside* the steel screen. The slight residual radioactivity in the steel screen can be guarded against by a 1-in. thick inner shield of mercury.

Plate XX shows the installation at the National Physical Laboratory, Teddington, England. In this, the steel screen is designed to hold several counters; it is 8 in. thick and weighs 23 tons. Anti-coincidence Geigers, mercury shield, and paraffin wax are all used in addition. A particular feature of this installation is the use of transistors where possible in the electrical circuitry, in order to obtain long-term stability and freedom from breakdowns.

6.5.4   *The Liquid Scintillator Method*

Certain organic substances (e.g. diphenyloxazole) have the property of emitting a flash of visible light when subjected to ionizing radiation. A few per cent of the scintillator is dissolved in an organic solvent (e.g. toluene, benzene, etc.) and the light flashes are detected by means of photomultipliers (see also Section 8.5). For radiocarbon detection, the solvent is synthesized from the sample, so that, as with the proportional counter method, the carbon under measurement forms an integral part of the apparatus. However, the chemical synthesis of suitable solvents is difficult, and although toluene has been prepared for this purpose, for routine work it is simpler to synthesize methanol (Pringle *et al.*, 1955; Delaney and McAulay, 1959). This is not a satisfactory solvent but up to 30 per cent can be added as a *diluent* to an ordinary scintillation solution before the scintillating properties are seriously impaired. The difficulty of synthesis is avoided altogether by Barendsen (1957) who uses liquid carbon dioxide as a diluent in a scintillator maintained at −20°C. Paraldehyde has also been synthesized for use as a diluent (Léger and Pichat, 1957), and benzene for use as a solvent (Tamers, 1960). A drawback of the latter synthesis is that only 10 per cent of the sample carbon is converted into benzene, giving rise to the possibility of fractionation error (see Section 6.5.2).

The advantage of the scintillation method over gas-counting techniques is the much smaller active volume of the detector for the same weight of carbon compared to the gas-counter methods. The background due to cosmic rays is roughly proportional to the active volume and consequently a much higher count to background ratio is obtainable. This is particularly valuable for very old samples (say, 20 000 years or more). There is, however, another limitation with the scintillator technique; this is the 'noise' pulses produced at the photo-cathode of the photomultiplier itself. The effect can be reduced by operation at low temperatures (e.g. in a deep freeze) and by use of two photomultipliers in coincidence so that the random 'noise' pulses are ignored.

6.5.5 *The Bubble Chamber Method*

A novel approach, following from work by Dodd (1955) and being investigated by Hall (1958), is the delayed boiling method. Again the carbon sample must be synthesized into an organic liquid which is then distilled into the volume of the 'counter'—in this case a very clean, fine bore glass tube. The temperature is raised above the normal boiling point but boiling is prevented by application of an excess pressure. Upon releasing the pressure there is a delay before boiling, because the bubbles have difficulty in finding a centre on which to form. The delay is less in the presence of an ionizing radiation because the charged ions are suitable centres. For ether that has been derived from 'dead' carbon (i.e. of mineral origin) the average delay is about 10 sec, but for 'modern' ether the average delay is only 3 sec. Effectively one is measuring the average time between carbon-14 disintegrations, and the delay for 'dead' carbon is analogous to the background in ordinary counters. Although, by automatic recycling, as many events can be timed as in ordinary methods, it seems unlikely that the bubble method will be a serious rival to more conventional methods owing to the added uncertainty introduced by the arbitrary point in time at which the delay period starts. The attractions of the method are the small volume of the counter with consequent low cosmic-ray background and the absence of complex electronics.

6.5.6   *Isotopic Enrichment*

The level of the counter background sets a practical limit of about 50 000 years to the age that can be determined. This can be extended by artificial enrichment of the carbon-14 relative to the carbon-12. The natural occurrence of this process has already been mentioned (see Section 6.4.5). In the laboratory it is accomplished by means of a thermal diffusion column—the same technique as used for the enrichment of fissile uranium-235 relative to uranium-238 in natural uranium. Vries and Haring (1958) have obtained an enrichment factor of twelve, corresponding to an increase of 20000 years in the limiting age. The size of sample necessary increases by the same factor. Another difficulty, inherent in any method of measuring very old samples, is the increased effect of contamination by modern carbon (see Fig. 6.4), whether during preparation or by seepage of humic liquids while still *in situ*. Haring, Vries and Vries (1958) found a measurable activity, corresponding to an age of 73000 years, in a sample prepared from anthracite which should have been completely inactive.

6.6   Other Radioisotopes Produced by Cosmic Rays

It is tempting to suppose that there may be other dating isotopes which will in the future rival carbon-14. This seems unlikely. One can hardly expect any other isotope to be of comparable abundance; a carbon-14 atom results from nearly every cosmic-ray neutron—and it is difficult to see how that can be improved on. It is true that the low level of radioactivity of natural carbon is due to the large size of the carbon reservoir but the carbon exchange cycle is necessary to achieve the world-wide near-uniform distribution.

The limitation of carbon dating to 70 000 years leaves a serious gap in the chronology of biological and geological development until about 10 million years ago when established geological radioactive methods (e.g. rubidium-87, thorium-232, uranium-235 and

-238) are applicable. The application of the potassium–argon method and of the ionium method has already been mentioned (Section 5.3.1.) Another possibility is beryllium-10 with a half-life of 2·5 million years. This is produced by cosmic rays, and is removed from the atmosphere in rain-water. It has been detected (Arnold 1956, Goel et al., 1957) in deep-ocean sediments. Unfortunately, according to Merrill, Honda and Arnold (1958), the residence time in the ocean is only a few hundred years, so that the initial concentration in the sediment is dependent on the sedimentation rate. Consequently dating is only possible if this rate is assumed constant, and this is not necessarily so.

At the other end of the time-scale there is tritium (hydrogen-3) with a half-life of 12·5 years, which has been mentioned in Section 6.2.2 as of use in determining ocean mixing rates. Another cosmic ray radioisotope that may be of value in oceanic studies is silicon-32. This has a half-life of 710 years and has been detected in siliceous sponges (Lal, Goldberg and Koide, 1960).

For a review of cosmic-ray isotopes and of cosmic-ray research in general, the reader is referred to Peters (1959).

6.7 Publication of Radiocarbon Dates

Up to 1959 lists of dates produced by laboratories all over the world were published in Science. This function has now been transferred to the American Journal of Science, Radiocarbon Supplement. The first volume of this contains a Bibliography of previous radiocarbon dating publications (Johnson, 1959).

Radiocarbon dates are also available on punched cards. Sorting notches in these cover such headings as latitude and longitude of sample, age, method of measurement, measuring laboratory, and scientific field to which the result is of interest (e.g. archæology, geophysics, oceanography, etc.) They are prepared by Radiocarbon Dates Association Inc., of Andover, Massachusetts.

6.8 Radiocarbon Laboratories

In general, a radiocarbon laboratory is engaged primarily on samples of particular interest to its parent institution, and other samples are accepted only by special arrangement. However, in Britain the National Physical Laboratory accepts a limited number of samples on payment of a fee (at present £50 per sample). In the United States, Isotopes Inc.,* accept samples on a commercial basis (present cost, $230 per sample).

* Isotopes Inc., 123 Woodland Avenue, Westwood, New Jersey.

A current list of dating laboratories appears from time to time in the *Radiocarbon Supplement*.

References

Anderson, E. C., Libby, W. F., Weinhouse, S., Reid, A. F., Kirschenbaum, A. D. and Grosse, A. V., 1947: Radiocarbon from cosmic radiation. *Science*, **105**, 576

Arnold, J. R., 1954: Scintillation counting of natural radiocarbon: I. The counting method. *Science*, **119**, 155–157

Arnold, J. R., 1956: Beryllium-10 produced by cosmic rays. *Science*, **124**, 584

Arnold, J. R. and Libby, W. F., 1949: Age determinations by radiocarbon content. Checks with samples of known age. *Science*, **110**, 678–680

Barendsen, G. W., 1957: Radiocarbon dating with liquid CO_2 as diluent in a scintillation solution. *Rev. sci. Instrum.* **28**, 430–432

Broecker, W. S. and Kulp, J. L., 1956: The radiocarbon method of age determination. *Amer. Antiq.*, **22**, 1–11

Broecker, W. S. and Olson, E. A., 1960: Radiocarbon from nuclear tests. *Science*, **132**, 712–721.

Burke, W. H., Jr. and Meinschein, W. G., 1955: C^{14} dating with a methane proportional counter. *Rev. sci. Instrum.*, **26**, 1137–1140

Craig, Harmon, 1954: Carbon-13 in plants and the relationships between Carbon-13 and Carbon-14 variations in nature. *J. Geol.*, **62**, 115–149

Craig, Harmon, 1957: The natural distribution of radiocarbon and the exchange time of carbon dioxide between atmosphere and sea. *Tellus*, **9**, 1–17

Deevey, E. S., Gross, M. S., Hutchinson, G. E. and Kraybill, H. L., 1954: The natural C^{14} contents of materials from hard-water lakes. *Proc. nat. Acad. Sci., Wash.*, **40**, 285–288

Delaney, C. F. G. and McAulay, I. R., 1959: A radiocarbon dating system using scintillation techniques. *Sci. Proc. R. Dublin Soc.* ser. A, **1**, no. 1

Dodd, C., 1955: Radiocarbon content and delayed boiling of liquids. *Proc. phys. Soc. Lond.* **B.68**, 686–689

Elliot, H., 1960: Cosmic Ray Intensity in Interplanetary Space. *Nature, Lond.*, **186**, 299–300

Elsasser, W., Ney, E. P. and Winckler, J. R., 1956: Cosmic ray intensity and geomagnetism. *Nature, Lond.*, **178**, 1226–1227

Fergusson, G. J., 1958: Reduction of atmospheric radiocarbon concentration by fossil fuel carbon dioxide and the mean life of carbon dioxide in the atmosphere. *Proc. roy. Soc. Lond.* **243A**, 561–574

Godwin, H., Walker, D. and Willis, E. H., 1957: Radiocarbon dating and post-glacial vegetational history. *Proc. roy. Soc. Lond.*, **B147**, 352–366

Goel, P. S., Kharkar, D. P., Lal, D., Narsappaya, N., Peters, B. and Yatirajam, V., 1957: The Beryllium-10 concentration in deep sea sediments. *Deep-Sea Research* **4**, 202–210

Grosse, A. V., Johnston, W. M., Wolfgang, R. L. and Libby, W. F., 1951: Tritium in nature. *Science*, **113**, 1–2

Hall, E. T., 1958: Some uses of Physics in Archæology. *Year Book of the Physical Society*, 1958, p. 31

Haring, A., de Vries, A. E. and de Vries, Hessel, 1958: Radiocarbon dating up to 70 000 years by isotopic enrichment. *Science*, **128**, 472–473

Hayes, F. N., Anderson, E. C. and Arnold, J. R., 1956: Liquid scintillation counting of natural radiocarbon. *U.N. Pub. 1956. IX.1, International Conference on the Peaceful Uses of Atomic Energy, 1st, Geneva 1955*, **14**, 188–192

Johnson, F., 1959: A bibliography of radiocarbon dating. *Amer. J. Sci., Radiocarbon Suppl.*, **1**, 199–214

Kulp, J. L. and Volchok, H. L., 1953: Constancy of cosmic ray flux over the past 30 000 years. *Phys. Rev.*, **90**, 713–714

Lal, D., Goldberg, E. D. and Koide, M., 1960: Cosmic-ray produced silicon-32 in nature. *Science*, **131**, 332–336

Léger, C. and Pichat, L., 1957: Utilization du paraldéhyde pour incorporer de grandes quantités de carbone marqué dans un scintillateur liquide. *C. R. Acad. Sci., Paris*, **244**, 190–192

Libby, W. F., 1946: Atmospheric helium three and radiocarbon from cosmic radiation. *Phys. Rev.*, **69**, 671–672

Libby, W. F., 1955: *Radiocarbon dating*, 2nd edn, University of Chicago Press, Chicago

Libby, W. F., 1959: Tritium in hydrology and meteorology. *Researches in Geochemistry* (ed. Abelson), 151–168

Libby, W. F., Anderson, E. C. and Arnold, J. R., 1949: Age determination by radiocarbon content: World-wide assay of natural radiocarbon. *Science*, **109**, 227–228

Merrill, J. R., Honda, M. and Arnold, J. R., 1958: Beryllium geochemistry and beryllium-10 age determination. *Proc. U.N. International Conference on the Peaceful Uses of Atomic Energy*, 2nd, Geneva, **2**, 251–254

Münnich, K. O., 1957: Heidelberg natural radiocarbon measurements—I. *Science*, **126**, 194–199

Peters, B., 1959: Progress in cosmic-ray research since 1947. *J. geophys. Res.*, **64**, 155–173

Pringle, R. W., Turchinetz, W. and Funt, B. L., 1955: Liquid scintillation techniques for radiocarbon dating. *Rev. sci. Instrum.*, **26**, 859–865

Ralph, E. K. and Stuckenrath, R., 1960: Carbon-14 Measurements of Known Age Samples. *Nature, Lond.*, **188**, 185–187

Suess, H. E., 1954: Natural radiocarbon measurements by acetylene counting. *Science*, **120**, 5–7

Suess, H. E., 1955: Radiocarbon concentration in modern wood. *Science*, **122**, 415–417

Tamers, M. A., 1960: Carbon-14 dating with the liquid scintillation counter. Total synthesis of the benzene solvent. *Science*, **132**, 668–669

Tauber, H., 1958: Difficulties in the application of C-14 results in archæology. *Archæologia Austriaca*, **24**, 59–69

Tauber, H., 1960: Latitudinal effect in the transport of radiocarbon from stratosphere to troposphere. *Radioisotopes in the Physical Sciences (Copenhagen Conference)* RICC/245. Internat. Atomic Energy Authority, Vienna

Vries, A. E. de and Haring, A., 1958: An improvement in age determination by the C^{14} method. *Proc. U.N. International Conference on the Peaceful Uses of Atomic Energy*, 2nd, Geneva, **2**, 249–250

Vries, Hessel de, 1958: Variation in concentration of radio-carbon with time and location on earth. *Koninkl. Nederlandse Akad. Wetensch. Proc.*, ser. B, **61**, 1–9

5+

Vries, Hessel de, 1959: Measurement and use of natural radiocarbon. *Researches in Geochemistry* (ed. Abelson), 169–189

Vries, Hessel de and Barendsen, G. W., 1953: Radiocarbon dating by a proportional counter filled with carbon dioxide. *Physica*, **19**, 987–1003

Vries, Hessel de, Barendsen, G. W. and Waterbolk, H. T., 1958: Groningen radiocarbon dates II. *Science*, **127**, 129–137

Vries, Hessel de, and Waterbolk, H. T., 1958: Groningen radiocarbon dates III. *Science*, **128**, 1550–1556

Willis, E. H., Tauber, H., Münnich, K. O., 1960: *Amer. J. Sci., Radiocarbon Suppl.*, **2**, 1–4.

Wright, H. E., 1957: The Late-Glacial chronology of Europe—a discussion. *Amer. J. Sci.*, **255**, 447–460

CHAPTER 7

MAGNETIC DATING

7.1 Introduction

The angle of declination, D, between magnetic north and geographic north, and the angle of dip, I, of a magnetic needle below
the horizontal, have been measured and recorded in London over
the past four centuries. This *secular variation* of D and I is shown
in Fig. 7.1, together with similar data for Paris, Rome and Boston.

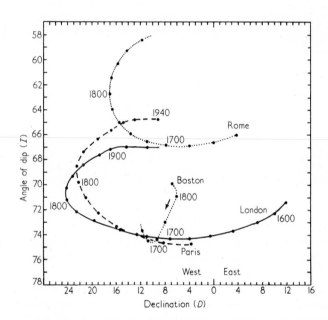

Fig. 7.1. Secular variation—London, Paris, Rome and Boston. The time scale is
indicated by dots at 20-year intervals. Prior to 1900 the curves shown are
those obtained by Bauer (1899) using recorded observations of declination
and dip to determine an empirical formula. Bauer's extrapolations into
periods when only declination was measured have been omitted. Subsequent
to 1900 the data has been taken from Vestine *et al.* (1947).

Besides the written record, this information is also stored in *baked
clay*. As we saw in Section 2.4.2, thermo-remanent magnetism is
acquired while clay is in the process of cooling down and remains

121

'frozen-in', once the clay is cold. The direction of this 'fossilized' magnetism is identical with that of the magnetic lines of force that caused it. Hence, measurement of the magnetic direction in clay that has remained *in situ* since it was baked (e.g. the walls of a pottery kiln) yields the values of D and I at the time of baking. Reference to Fig. 7.1 then gives the *date* of baking. The magnetic direction is determined by laboratory measurements on samples extracted from the archæological feature; geographic north, and the horizontal, are carefully marked on the samples prior to removal.

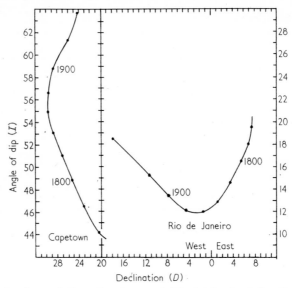

Fig. 7.2. Secular variation—Capetown and Rio de Janeiro (after Bauer (1899) and Vestine *et al.* (1947)).

There are two major drawbacks. First, the directly recorded data of Fig. 7.1 goes back only to the end of the sixteenth century; to use the method for earlier periods requires *calibration*—the determination of D and I from baked clay samples of known date. Such measurements falsify any hopes that the curves of Fig. 7.1 exhibit a regular periodicity. Secondly, calibration is necessary for each particular geographic region. The secular variation arises, in part, from effects near the surface of the earth's core (see Section 2.2.3), and extrapolation is only possible, at the very most, up to distances of a thousand miles (compare Figs. 7.1 and 7.2). It follows that to establish a magnetic dating system for a given region and a given era involves many preliminary measurements; however, in addition to their eventual archæological value, such measurements are of immediate intrinsic interest as experimental data which any theories of the origin of the earth's magnetism must be able to explain.

Baked clay of archæological origin, besides its occurrence in kilns, is of course the material of the pottery and bricks produced in them. If a pot is heavily glazed or carries elaborate ornamentation, it may be valid to assume that it was baked standing upright on its base, or in some cases inverted on its mouth. The angle of dip can then be found. This type of work was pioneered at the end of the nineteenth century by Folgheraiter (1899). Although his results are unreliable because of the crudeness of his measuring apparatus, his discussion of principles is pertinent. He points out that the stability of the remanent magnetism is proven by the differing magnetic directions of the bricks of an ancient wall, or by the similar angles of dip (with respect to the base) that he found in some Arétine vases which had been buried pell-mell for over 2000 years.

Folgheraiter also attempted to determine the past magnetic field *intensity* by the technique of thermal remagnetization (see Section 7.5.5). Baked clay that is reheated loses its original magnetization and acquires a new one in the magnetic field in which it cools. The ratio of the original to the new magnetic moment gives the ratio of the two field strengths. The conditions necessary for valid results have now been established by Thellier, after a long period of careful research (Thellier and Thellier, 1959); his measurements indicate that, in France, the earth's magnetic intensity 2000 years ago was nearly twice its present value. This is in concordance with the observation that between 1922 and 1945 the magnetic moment of the earth decreased by 1 per cent.

Unfortunately the thermal remagnetization technique, if undertaken properly, is extremely tedious. However, besides its intrinsic geophysical interest, the curve representing the variation of intensity with time is valuable for dating because it can resolve ambiguities resulting from the occurrence in different eras of the same pair of values of D and I. An additional interest attached to intensity measurements is the connection with radiocarbon dating; if the enhanced intensity was a world-wide effect, then the magnetic deflection of cosmic-ray particles away from the earth would have been greater, thereby reducing the production rate of radiocarbon.

Archæological magnetic dating ('Archæomagnetism') is an offshoot of rock magnetism ('Palæomagnetism'). Igneous rocks acquire remanent magnetism on cooling from the molten state and consequently give information about the earth's magnetic field in geological times; sedimentary rocks exhibit remanent magnetism too, acquired as the particles are deposited. One remarkable conclusion is that the earth's magnetic field has completely *reversed* in direction on a number of occasions. In addition palæomagnetic measurements suggest that there has been considerable *drifting* of continents with respect to one another, and also that the axis of rotation has moved with respect to the earth's crust as a whole ('*polar wandering*').

7.1.1   *Archæological Application*

Before discussing the properties of remanent magnetism and their practical application, the following points are summarized:

(*i*) The past *direction* is easier to determine than the past *intensity*, and a measurable change in the former occurs within a shorter period than in the latter. To be of use, the error in determining the direction must not be much greater than 1°.

(*ii*) The best type of sample is from the baked clay of a structure (e.g. kilns, ovens, hearths) for which the possibility of subsidence can be ruled out. Because the distortion of the field direction by the magnetism of the burnt material itself is not negligible, the average of as many samples as possible is desirable.

(*iii*) Large bricks and tiles, and heavily ornamentated and glazed pottery can be used to determine the past angle of dip (and also the past intensity), but such measurements are valueless unless there is evidence as to the geographical origin. The bricks of a building would almost certainly be baked nearby, but pots may have been traded from afar, particularly if of high craftsmanship.

(*iv*) If the angle of dip is near to 45° then it is not obvious which face of a brick was horizontal during baking, and the method is not applicable. For other angles of dip, many samples must be taken in order to average out irregularity in stacking. The same applies to pots.

(*v*) In samples which have not been baked to a high temperature, magnetization subsequently acquired may be important, and special 'washing' techniques are necessary (see Section 7.5.4).

(*vi*) Sample taking is pointless unless there is reliable association of the burnt feature with significant archæological evidence.

7.2   The Thermo-Remanent Magnetism of Baked Clay

Earlier in this book (Section 2.4.2) we have been concerned with the crude disturbance to the earth's magnetic field that is produced by the thermo-remanent magnetization of a feature that has been heated. The finer details now need examination. The primary question is whether the *direction* of magnetization of a sample measured in the laboratory today accurately represents the direction of the earth's field in which it was baked, perhaps several thousand years ago. This will depend not only on the stability of the original thermo-remanent magnetism, but also on the relative importance of any secondary magnetizations acquired during the long period the sample has remained *in situ*, or during transportation to the laboratory. Secondly, in deducing the past intensity of the earth's field, the factors governing the intensity of magnetization acquired by a given piece of clay are important.

Besides being the commonest archæological material, baked clay is also the most satisfactory for magnetic dating. Baked soil is difficult to collect as a coherent sample, and burnt stones, even if sufficiently magnetic (limestone usually contains very little iron), are not as reliable, although 'rock magnetism' is the whole basis of palæomagnetic studies (see Section 7.8). Metallic iron is useless; the direction of its magnetization is strongly influenced by the shape of the object and it is not stable.

The remanent magnetism of baked clay has been studied extensively at l'Institut de Physique du Globe, in Paris, by Professor E. Thellier, since 1933 (see references). The outstanding properties of thermo-remanent magnetism (henceforth abbreviated to TRM) are summarized below.

7.2.1 The direction of the TRM is the same as that of the magnetic field (as long as any local field due to the magnetism of the clay itself is small; ideally this requires the specific magnetization to be less than 10^{-3} emu/c.c but in practice much stronger magnetizations are tolerable).

7.2.2 The intensity of TRM is proportional to the magnetic field strength for given thermal conditions (excluding magnetic fields very much stronger than encountered naturally).

7.2.3 The intensity (after cooling) increases with the temperature of baking, up to a limiting value reached when the baking temperature is 675°C (see Fig. 7.3).

7.2.4 A second heating, in a different magnetic field, to the maximum temperature reached during the first (or 675°C, whichever is lower) destroys all trace of the original magnetization.

7.2.5   The partial TRM, $M(T_1, T_2)$ acquired as the sample cooled from T_1 to T_2, is unaltered as long as the temperature subsequently remains below T_2, and is completely destroyed if the temperature reaches T_1. Thus, in Fig. 7.3, if after the first cooling

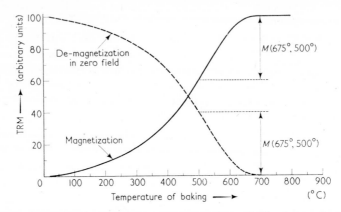

FIG. 7.3. Acquisition of thermo-remanent magnetism—idealized curve for baked clay. The full curve shows the magnetization (measured at 20°C) acquired in cooling to 20°C from the temperature indicated by the horizontal scale, in a magnetic field. After the final cooling from above 675°C the sample has been gradually demagnetized by cooling in zero field. The magnetization (measured at 20°C) remaining after coolings from successively increasing temperatures is shown by the broken curve.

The shape of the curves depends on the composition of the sample. However, the demagnetization curve is always the mirror image of the magnetization curve in the line through 50 on the vertical scale.

from above 675°C, the sample is subsequently reheated to 500°C (say) and then allowed to cool in a space where the magnetic field strength is zero (by artificial annulment), the TRM remaining is $M(675°C, 500°)$ as indicated. The dotted curve shows the effect of such demagnetization for successively increasing temperatures.

7.2.6   The carriers that acquire magnetization within a given temperature interval lose it, on demagnetization, in the same temperature interval. This explains why the *amount* acquired is equal to the amount lost, as stated in 7.2.5, but it implies also that if after a first heating with a certain orientation of the sample, there is a second heating to a lower temperature and with a different orientation, the two superposed magnetizations can be separated, by careful demagnetization, in both magnitude *and direction*. The vectors in Fig. 7.4 represent two such magnetizations. Archæologically, $M(675°, 400°)$ might derive from the initial baking of a vase, the full magnetization having been partially destroyed by a second heating to 400°C, perhaps for the purpose of firing the glaze, but in a different orientation with respect to the magnetic field. Thus $M(400°, 20°)$ is in a different direction to $M(675°, 400°)$ and the *resultant*, actually observed, is in a different direction still. If the vase is now cooled in zero field from successively increasing temperatures, the direction of remaining magnetization, found after each cooling, gradually swings round to the direction of $M(675°, 400°)$. When the reheating temperature exceeds 400°C there is no further change in the *direction* of the resultant, only a reduction in the magnitude as $M(675°, 400°)$ is gradually eaten away. Thus, not only can the two directions be found, but also the *temperature* of the second heating (as long as it did not exceed that of the first, or 675°C, whichever is the lower).

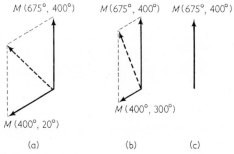

Fig. 7.4. Vector addition of TRM. (a) The observed magnetization is the resultant of that acquired between 675°C and 400°C during the initial firing and that acquired between 400°C and 20°C during a second heating when the orientation of the sample was different. (b) That part of the secondary magnetization acquired between 300°C and 20°C has been removed by cooling from 300°C in zero field. (c) By cooling from 400°C in zero field, all of the secondary magnetization has been removed.

An extreme case of superposition is two equal TRM's, acquired in different temperature ranges, at 180° to one another. The resultant is nil initially, but if the demagnetization procedure is applied, a magnetic moment *develops*!

7.2.7 Although the major part of the magnetization is acquired well above normal temperatures, that acquired in cooling, between say 40°C and 20°C, is not always negligible. For one set of baked bricks examined by Thellier, the remanent magnetization acquired in that range amounted to 1 per cent of the total, on the average (Thellier and Thellier, 1959, p. 318); for another set the average moment acquired between 60°C and 20°C was 5 per cent (*loc. cit.* p. 325), but this is exceptional.

A more important effect, as far as measurement is concerned, is the temporary (or *reversible*) change of M with temperature.

5*

This refers to the variation at normal temperatures, of the magnetization acquired at a high temperature, and for the first set of samples Thellier found a change of 0·3 per cent per °C.

7.2.8   The TRM acquired by a sample on cooling from 675°C is usually an order of magnitude larger than the instantaneous magnetization induced in the sample by the same field at normal temperatures.

7.2.9   No measurable decay with time has been detected over a period of several years. Stability of direction over thousands of years is demonstrated by pots and bricks which have been stored in a position such that their magnetization is not parallel to the earth's field.

7.2.10   The magnetization is unaltered by the application of opposing magnetic fields unless the applied field strength is several hundred oersteds or more.

7.3   The Mechanism Responsible

The *Curie Point* is the temperature above which the ability to retain remanent magnetism disappears (i.e. above this temperature a substance ceases to exhibit ferromagnetic properties). Fig. 7.3 suggests that the magnetic constituents of baked clay exhibit a wide range of Curie points, from room temperature up to 675°C. This temperature is in fact the Curie point for pure hæmatite. For an artificially prepared sample of hæmatite, 90 per cent of the TRM is acquired in the ten degrees below the Curie point. For magnetite this range is 17° and the Curie point is at 565°C (Roquet, 1954).

Variation of the Curie point is not tenable theoretically, and a more satisfactory interpretation (see Néel, 1955) is in terms of the *blocking temperature*, T_B. Above this temperature the magnetic domains are able to realign as dictated by the direction of the external magnetic field, while below it they are 'frozen'.

7.3.1   *Single-Domain Grains*

The size of hæmatite grains dispersed in clay is small enough (perhaps 10^{-5} to 10^{-6} cm) to consider each grain as a single magnetic domain, spontaneously magnetized along a direction dictated by the shape, or crystalline anisotropy, of the grain. The intensity of the spontaneous magnetization is unaffected by an applied field, but, if the temperature is high enough, its direction can reverse so that its component along the field direction is parallel rather than anti-parallel (see Fig. 2.4). This reversal is possible when the thermal agitation energy of the grain is comparable with the potential energy of the constraints tending to keep the magnetization along the preferred axis of the grain. The probability of reversal is a very sharply rising function of temperature, and it is possible to define the blocking temperature, T_B, above which there is a high probability of reversal in a few seconds, and below which, reversal is only likely in a very long time. T_B is proportional to the volume of the grain, and consequently the variation of T_B necessary to account for the thermal memory of Section 7.2.6 is easily explained as variation of grain size.

Thermal agitation does not favour any particular direction, and tends to destroy any preferential alignment. Since the magnetic torque exerted on the domain by the external field is small (except for fields well in excess of an oersted), the alignment achieved by the field is far from complete. The fractional excess of domains with a component in the field direction is proportional to $(\mu F/kT_B)$ as in the case of the alignment of protons (see Section 3.2.1). When the temperature falls below T_B, and reversal is no longer possible, this equilibrium excess is 'frozen', and is the cause of the remanent magnetization. After 'freezing', the intensity increases as the temperature falls (see Section 7.2.7); this is not due to change of domain directions, but due to an increase in the spontaneous magnetization of each individual domain.

7.3.2 *Multi-Domain Grains*

For magnetite the grains (10^{-4} to 10^{-2} cm) are too big to contain only a single domain. The magnetization of a magnetite grain is therefore the resultant of a number of domain magnetizations differently orientated. Nevertheless, magnetite exhibits similar TRM properties to hæmatite. Theoretical interpretations have been given by Néel (1955) and Stacey (1958). In these, above the blocking temperature the magnetization of the grain is such that, within the grain, the internal field exactly cancels the applied field; consequently the resultant magnetization of the grain is proportional to the latter, as fits observation. Below the blocking temperature, the thermal energy is no longer sufficient for domain rearrangement and the resultant direction is retained; the intensity increases as the temperature falls, as before, because of the growth of spontaneous domain magnetization.

The TRM of multi-domain grains has also been considered by Verhoogen (1959) who suggests that strains in the crystal structure of the mineral are a necessary condition for high blocking temperatures. In this way he explains why the TRM of intrusive rocks, such as granite, which have cooled slowly from the molten state, is weak compared to that of extrusive rocks, such as lava and basalt, which have chilled too rapidly for annealing to take place.

7.4   Remanent Magnetizations acquired at Normal Temperatures

Magnetic dating rests on the assumption that the remanent magnetization of the sample records information about the earth's field existing when the feature cooled down for the last time. If this last cooling did not correspond to the archæologically-assumed use of the feature, that is not a fault of the scientific technique. There is also the possibility of secondary magnetization having been acquired through minor reheatings due, for example, to an accidental fire; such effects can be separated out by thermal demagnetization (see Section 7.2.6), and their occurrence is likely to be suspected from visual inspection of the archæological feature. But in addition there are three causes from which remanent magnetization can be acquired without heating: *time, chemical change*, and *strong magnetic fields*.

Fortunately such effects are either negligible or absent in most samples of baked clay. But in some cases they may cause small errors, and in others the results may be completely incomprehensible.

7.4.1   *Viscous Remanent Magnetism*

The blocking temperature, T_B, has been explained as the temperature at which thermal agitation causes continual domain reversal in single-domain grains, and domain rearrangement in multi-domain grains. There will be some grains for which T_B is below normal temperatures. Such grains follow changes in the applied field direction and exhibit no remanent effects. However, grains for which T_B is in the temperature range immediately above room temperature, exhibit a sort of magnetic 'viscosity'; a remanent magnetism builds up as the time of application of the external field is prolonged, and if the external field is removed, the remanent magnetism decays away. This viscosity effect arises because although the *average* thermal agitation energy of a grain is insufficient to overcome the constraining forces, there is a finite probability that each grain will at some time possess an above-average thermal energy. There is some similarity here with evaporation from a liquid well below its boiling point; on the average the molecules do not have enough kinetic energy to escape from the surface, but, because for short intervals a few of the molecules have energies well in excess of the average, evaporation takes place.

As the time of observation is prolonged, the chance of a given excess thermal energy grows, and more grains are affected, and also those with higher values of T_B. Experimentally it is found that the remanent magnetization is proportional to the logarithm of the time, excluding an initial period of up to 20 sec.

This has the fortunate consequence that the growth (or decay) of viscous magnetization observed in a sample between $t = 10$ min and $t = 14$ days, is equal to the amount acquired between $t = 14$ days and $t = 90$ years, or between $t = 90$ years and $t = 200\,000$ years. Thus observation of the change of magnetization during a few weeks of laboratory storage indicates whether or not the viscous magnetization acquired since archæological times is appreciable.

The storage changes found by Thellier and Thellier (1959, p. 316) for baked clay samples from Roman kilns were small; the average change for five kilns (totalling 49 samples) was less than 1 per cent of the total magnetization, for three other kilns (totalling 26 samples) the change was less than 2 per cent, and for one kiln (4 samples) the average change was 4·5 per cent. On the other hand for basalt and metamorphic clay changes of up to 16 per cent occurred. Viscous magnetization is easily removed by heating to 60°C, for instance, and cooling in zero field; this leaves the major part of the TRM intact, and in any case it is desirable to eliminate the TRM acquired below 60°C, since it is likely to have arisen from a secondary heating.

7.4.2 Chemical Magnetization

The occurrence, within a sample, of a chemical change whereby a magnetic mineral is formed, results in a remanent magnetization in a direction dictated by the existing external field direction. Such chemical remanence (Haigh, 1959) shows the high stability of TRM and cannot be separated. Consequently, the magnetization of a sample in which this has happened will be mistaken for TRM. The field direction deduced will not be that corresponding to the time of last cooling but to some later period.

Fortunately, in well-baked clay, such chemical changes are unlikely to occur spontaneously, since such material is remarkably stable on reheating. However, the impregnation of a sample with organic matter, or prolonged immersion in water, could lead to such parasitic effects.

7.4.3 *Strong External Fields*

At normal temperatures, the direction of magnetization of the single-domain grains of hæmatite cannot be reversed except by magnetic fields of several thousand oersted. In the multi-domain grains of magnetite, domain rearrangement is possible, and the *coercive force* is less—several hundred oersted. The resulting magnetization is termed 'isothermal remanent magnetism' and it can be produced in baked clay by flashes of lightning. Fortunately it can be separated from TRM, either by alternating field 'washing' or by thermal 'washing' (Section 7.5.4.)

Anhysteric remanent magnetization can also be produced by lightning. This occurs when a strong alternating field acts in the presence of a weak steady field (such as the earth's field). It is remarkably stable to thermal 'washing' but can be separated from TRM by alternating field 'washing'.

7.5 Practical Procedures

Before embarking, in any particular case, on the appreciable labour involved in magnetic dating, it is wise to ask what benefit it is going to be. A date can only be obtained if the secular variation curve has been established for the region in question. For the purpose of building up the curve, samples are only acceptable if in association with reliable archæological dating evidence; otherwise they are valueless and misleading.

7.5.1 *Suitability of Material*

For an archæologist faced with the question of which burnt features on his site are suitable for magnetic dating, the prime consideration is whether any movement has occurred since baking. If the structure has tilted as a whole, samples from different parts of it will give results, which though consistent, are in error by an unknown amount. Secondly, there is the practical question of whether the samples can be extracted without breaking. Thirdly, they should be well-baked and free from impregnation by organic matter.

The distortion of the magnetic field by the local field of the structure itself, though it cannot be overlooked, is not as serious as is suggested by measurements made when the structure is cold and the full remanent magnetism has developed. The direction acquired at higher temperatures is likely to be more faithful than at lower ones; although the latter can be erased by thermal demagnetization, this is an undesirable extra labour in most cases. Errors from local fields can also be eliminated by averaging over a sufficient number of samples; at least five are necessary from any one structure, and up to twenty are desirable.

For samples not found in the position of baking, e.g. bricks and pottery, the justification for assuming a certain position, with respect to the horizontal, must be examined. Magnetic measurements will reveal the validity of this assumption as long as a sufficient number of similar specimens are available. With pottery there is also the question of the geographical region of origin (to within a few hundred miles).

7.5.2 Sample Extraction from Structures

Samples of weak mechanical strength are partially encased in gypsum plaster (or plaster of paris) before being detached from the

(*Ph.*: Thomas Thompson, Tonbridge)

PLATE XXI. Magnetic dating—levelling the sample frame. On the right is a completed sample ready for detachment. In making the trench to accommodate the frame great care is taken to avoid disturbance of the 'stump' of baked clay inside it.

structure. To do this a miniature square 'ditch' is dug leaving the sample as a stump in the middle, about 3 in. × 3 in. The square frame (see Plate XXI) is placed in the 'ditch' and levelled. Plaster is then poured in and the top surface smoothed off flush with the top of the frame. When the plaster has set a line is sighted from a nearby theodolite (Plate XXII) and marked on the surface. The

(*Ph.:* Thomas Thompson, Tonbridge)

PLATE XXII. Magnetic dating—sighting from the theodolite. The orientation of the theodolite is determined by shooting the sun. A line is then sighted on the top surface of the sample and its direction on the theodolite azimuth scale is noted.

theodolite orientation is found by shooting the sun at a known time and using suitable astronomical tables (e.g. *The Star Almanac for Land Surveyors*, published in London by Her Majesty's Stationery Office together with *Tables of Computed Altitude and Azimuth*, published by U.S. Navy Hydrographic Office). The present-day direction of magnetic north is also marked on the sample by means of a trough compass as a check of local field distortion. Finally, the sample is detached from the structure by cutting away underneath the frame.

For samples of good mechanical strength the frame may not be necessary but the orientation is best marked on a horizontal plaster surface as before. This can be formed either with the frame or by pressing on a lump of just-plastic plaster with a flat plate.

(*Ph.*: M. J. Aitken)

PLATE XXIII. Magnetic dating—marking the sample. The single arrow marks the theodolite direction. The pair of arrows are the direction of *existing* magnetic North, marked on as a check of local field distortion.

After removal of the sample it is desirable to enclose it completely in plaster as protection during transportation. The remanent magnetism itself is unaffected by mechanical shock but strong magnetic fields and elevated temperatures are to be avoided.

7.5.3 *Storage*

Before measurement each sample is stored for several weeks in the same position, with respect to the magnetic field, as it was found in the feature. This reconstitutes any viscous magnetization that was lost during transportation, and allows any then acquired to die away. Using one of the magnetometers described in Section 7.6 the components of the magnetization in three perpendicular directions are measured: the vertical direction, existing magnetic north (as marked on the sample) and magnetic east. The sample is now stored in the *inverse* position: upside down and with its magnetic north direction pointing magnetic south. After several weeks the sample is measured again; the *changes* in the northward and the vertical components represent twice the contributions of the viscous magnetization acquired during the storage period. After allowance for this the direction of the thermo-remanent contribution can be deduced with respect to the top face of the sample and the theodolite direction marked on it. In most cases the viscous component is negligible; where it exceeds 2 per cent of the whole, further checks may be necessary.

If the temperatures at which the two sets of measurements are made differ by more than 1°C, effects due to changes in the spontaneous domain magnetization (see Section 7.2.7) may become important. A method of storage which avoids the necessity for strict temperature control is to use the *reverse* position during the second period: magnetic north points magnetic south, as before, but the sample is kept right way up. The vertical component then acts as a reference and any change in the values of the horizontal components, relative to the vertical one, indicates viscous effects.

7.5.4 'Washing' Techniques

The storage procedure described above reveals the seriousness of any viscous effects, but not the presence of any secondary thermal magnetizations. These might arise from elevated temperatures during transportation, or, *in situ* from climatic variations or fortuitous fires, or in the case of a pot, from use in cremation or cooking. Erasure of the magnetization acquired below 60°C (say) by thermal demagnetization from that temperature (see Section 7.5.5) deals with the first two causes, which in any case are usually negligible (but see Section 7.2.7). The other possibilities can only be checked by the laborious process of thermal demagnetization from successively increasing temperatures (see Section 7.2.6).

An alternative to thermal 'washing' is demagnetization by an applied alternating magnetic field, the earth's field being annulled (Thellier and Rimbert, 1955). This is widely used in the study of rock magnetism. The high temperature thermo-remanent magnetism is carried by grains of high blocking temperature, and at normal temperatures these are unaffected except by magnetic fields of several hundred oersted or more, but the isothermal and anhysteric magnetizations (Section 7.4.3) are destroyed when the alternating field reaches the same value as the fields which produced them (Rimbert, 1956a, 1957). Isothermal magnetization can be separated by thermal 'washing' also, but this is not the case for anhysteric magnetization.

Viscous magnetization can be removed by alternating field 'washing'; the field necessary increases as the logarithm of the time over which the viscous magnetization was acquired (Rimbert, 1956b).

During alternating field 'washing', it is essential that the earth's field is reduced to zero, by annulment with Helmholtz coils, in order to avoid producing an anhysteric magnetization in the process. It is also important that the sample is removed from the alternating field very gradually. Otherwise parasitic magnetizations will be produced (Thellier and Rimbert, 1954).

7.5.5 Thermal Remagnetization

In principle thermal demagnetization from a temperature T_1 means the cooling of the samples in zero magnetic field, from T_1 to the standard room temperature of 20°C. The magnetization remaining is then $M(675°, F_0, T_1)$, where F_0 was the magnetic field strength during the archæological cooling and it is assumed that the temperature then attained was 675°C or greater. In practice it is difficult to maintain the annulment of the earth's field in the laboratory with sufficient accuracy over the time of cooling, and it is better to follow the procedure developed by Thellier and Thellier (1959, p. 318).

The sample is first cooled from T_1, in the earth's field, F_L, of the laboratory and the magnetization measured. It is $M(670°, F_0, T_1)$ plus $M(T_1, F_L, 20°)$. The sample is then cooled from T_1 but in the inverse position (see Section 7.5.3). The magnetization is now $M(670°, F_0, T_1)$ minus $M(T_1, F_L, 20°)$. Hence subtraction yields twice $M(T_1, F_L, 20°)$ and the average is $M(670°, F_0, T_1)$, the magnetization that would have remained on cooling from T_1, in zero field. By pairs of coolings from successively increasing values of T_1, the magnetization corresponding to any desired temperature interval can be determined.

The oven used must be constructed entirely of non-magnetic materials and the electric heater windings must be non-inductive; otherwise parasitic magnetizations may be produced under the action of alternating magnetic fields. Gas fired ovens avoid this trouble but the control of temperature is more difficult.

For the above procedure to be valid, it is important that no chemical changes (in the magnetic constituents) take place during heating; this can be checked by measuring $M(T_1, F_L, 20°)$ after each successive heating to T_2, T_3, etc. Fortunately well reddened (and therefore highly oxidized) samples of hard baked clay are remarkably stable if heated in air. For grey reduced clay, an atmosphere of nitrogen may be necessary. One possible cause of instability is the presence in the sample of maghæmite (γ-Fe_2O_3) produced by intruding organic matter; maghæmite converts to hæmatite (α-Fe_2O_3) on heating above several hundred degrees.

In the absence of any chemical changes, the past intensity of the earth's field is given by the relation

$$\frac{F_0}{F_L} = \frac{M(T_2, F_0, T_1)}{M(T_2, F_L, T_1)} \qquad (7.1)$$

If this ratio is the same for all temperature intervals ($T_1 T_2$, $T_2 T_3$, $T_3 T_4$, etc.) this in itself is evidence that no changes have taken place above T_2. Changes are unlikely at the lower temperatures and varying ratios in this range are more likely to arise from secondary magnetizations.

It is essential that the whole volume of the sample is uniformly baked. If, for instance, there is some unbaked clay present, the moment acquired on remagnetization in the laboratory will be anomalously high.

7.6 Measuring Apparatus

The goal is to measure, for each sample, the remanent direction to within $\frac{1}{2}°$ and the intensity to within $\frac{1}{2}$ per cent, or better. Although a number of magnetometers have been developed in palæomagnetic work for measuring very weak remanent magnetizations in rock samples, such instruments are not directly applicable to archæological samples; firstly, because the accuracy required is higher, and secondly because the sample size is different. Small samples of only an inch across can be obtained from rocks by coring with a diamond cutter. This is ruled out for archæological samples by their heterogeneous nature (besides this, accurate directional markings cannot be retained on a small sample) and the sample must be measured as a whole. Samples taken *in situ* are usually encased in plaster and measure at least 4 in. × 4in. × 4 in. Bricks and pottery are larger, and for this type of work the instrument must be able to deal with sample dimensions up to 12 inches at least. Size is important because, unless the sample is positioned a long way away from the detector, it cannot be regarded as a simple bar magnet.

The total magnetic moments of samples vary between several units (emu) for well-baked bricks to less than 10^{-3} emu for pottery made from refined clay. The proton magnetometer described in Chapter 3 is not suitable for this type of work because it is insufficiently sensitive for many samples. For the standard instrument the lower limit is 0·5 gamma, and even if modifications were made to reduce this to 0·1 gamma (10^{-6} oersteds) the field due to a sample of moment 0·1 emu would barely be detectable when 50 cm away, let alone measurable.

7.6.1 *Astatic Magnetometers*

The simplest and most sensitive instrument used in rock magnetism consists of two bar magnets of equal strength fixed rigidly
at either end of a rod about 4-in. long (see Fig. 7.5) and suspended
by a fine fibre of phosphor-bronze or quartz. Since the two magnets are anti-parallel the torque due to the earth's field on the

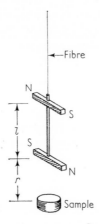

←—Fibre

Fig. 7.5. Simple astatic magnetometer. Restoring torque due to a uniform (e.g.
the earth's) field is eliminated by using magnets of equal moment. There is a
deflection due to the field of the sample, however, because it is nearer to the
lower magnet than to the upper one.

upper one exactly cancels out that on the lower one; on the other
hand, the torque on the lower magnet due to a small sample held
a distance r beneath it is greater than that on the upper one by a
factor $[(r+l)/r]^3$ where l is the separation of the astatic pair. Thus
for r equal to l, the net torque on the pair is nearly 90 per cent of
the torque on the lower one. The resultant deflection depends on
the restoring torque of the fibre (which can be less than 10^{-2} dyne
cm per radian), and on the accuracy to which the moments of the
two magnets have been balanced (the 'degree of astatizing';
better than one part in 5000 can be achieved). With careful design
and construction, the field due to samples having moments of
only 10^{-7} emu can be detected (see, for example, Blackett, 1952).

By observing the deflection, the sample's magnetic component
that is perpendicular to the direction of the two magnets can be
deduced. The components in two other directions are found by
altering the orientation of the sample and the resultant vector is
obtained. The effect of any instantaneously induced magnetization

can be eliminated either by arranging that the equilibrium direction of the astatic magnets is north–south, or by annulling the horizontal component of the earth's field by means of current-carrying coils on either side of the apparatus. However, there still remains the possibility of a magnetization being induced in the sample by the field of the lower magnet itself, and this limits the permissible moment.

The difficulty in applying the instrument to archæological work is that if the sample is of irregular shape or composition, the field due to it is parallel to the direction of magnetization only at distances much larger than the dimensions of the sample. Besides reducing sensitivity the requirements in laboratory space would be intolerable. However it is possible to make measurements at a distance of the same order as the sample dimensions as long as readings are taken for a number of sample orientations planned so as to average out the effects of irregular shape. Instruments of the astatic type are currently used for archæological measurements at the Museum of Classical Archæology, Cambridge University, and at the Science Faculty of Tokyo University.

Another drawback is the need to avoid vibrational and magnetic disturbance; steel-framed buildings are to be avoided, and also proximity to electric trains or heavy traffic. Although there is no resultant torque on the astatic pair from the earth's field, this is no longer so if there is a slight vertical gradient such as will occur with a locally-produced field. The effect can be lessened by using *three* magnets as shown in Fig. 7.6; the upper and lower moments

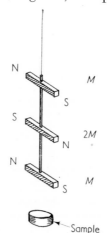

Fɪɢ. 7.6. 'Parastatic' magnetometer. This arrangement eliminates disturbances due to fields having a uniform vertical gradient as well as disturbances due to uniform fields.

are equal and anti-parallel to the middle moment which is of double strength. With this arrangement ('*para*static') there is zero torque in a non-uniform field as long as the *gradient* is uniform.

A crude form of the astatic instrument can be simply constructed from two laboratory magnets fixed at either end of a dural rod and suspended on a thin nylon thread. By tilting one of the magnets, the components of the moments in the horizontal direction can be balanced to 1 part in 200 without difficulty (corresponding to a ratio of 20 between the times of oscillations with moments parallel and anti-parallel). A sample of moment 0·1 emu will cause an appreciable deflection when held 3 in. below the lower magnet.

7.6.2 *Ballistic Magnetometers*

Movement of a magnet near to a coil of wire induces a voltage across the ends of the coil; this is the phenomenon of electromagnetic induction and it occurs whenever there is a change in the number of lines of force threading an electrical circuit. The voltage is proportional to the *rate* of change, but if the coil is connected to a ballistic galvanometer the effect can be integrated. A sharp change in the number of lines of force linking the circuit ('the flux linkage') causes a 'throw' of the ballistic galvanometer which is proportional to the *total* change (as long as the change occurs before appreciable deflection of the galvanometer has taken place). Consider a short bar magnet of moment m, situated at the centre of a circular coil of N turns of average radius a. If the magnet is perpendicular to the plane of the coil then the flux linkage is given by

$$\phi = \frac{2\pi m}{a}N \qquad (7.2)$$

If the coil is connected to a ballistic galvanometer, the total circuit resistance being R, the electric charge that flows through the galvanometer when the magnet is quickly removed is given by

$$q = \frac{\phi}{R} = \frac{2\pi m N}{Ra} \qquad (7.3)$$

The 'throw' of the ballistic galvanometer is proportional to q. If the direction of the magnet is quickly reversed, the total change in ϕ is twice this, and the net charge that flows through a ballistic galvanometer connected across the ends of the coil is given by

$$q = \frac{\phi_1 - \phi_2}{R} = \frac{4\pi m N}{Ra} \qquad (7.4)$$

On the other hand, if the initial and final directions of the magnet are in the plane of the coil, the initial and final flux linkages are zero, and the net flow of charge is zero also. Hence by rotating a magnetized sample through 180°, quickly, the component of the magnetization initially along the axis of the coil can be determined. In principle, the direction of magnetization can be found by altering the starting position of the sample until the galvanometer deflection, resulting from reversal of the sample, is zero. In practice this null method is unsatisfactory because although the net change of flux is zero, during the rotation large positive and negative changes occur and their effects do not cancel exactly unless the reversal time is infinitely short. Instead, the components in three perpendicular directions are measured, and from these, the magnitude and direction of the resultant is determined.

The flux linkage given by equation (7.2) only applies to a magnet at the centre of the coil; elsewhere it is different and hence the finite size of the sample, compared to the radius of the coil, immediately raises a difficulty. This can be overcome by using a pair of coaxial coils connected in series after the manner of Helmholtz. In the apparatus used at l'Institut de Physique du Globe, Paris (Thellier, 1938), the coil radius is 30 cm and the spacing between coils is 36 cm; reversal of a magnet produces a net flux charge in the coils which is the same to within 2 per cent, as long as the magnet is within a spherical region around the midpoint of the system, of radius 10 cm.

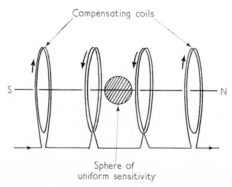

FIG. 7.7. Helmholtz coils with compensation (after Thellier, 1938). The two outer coils are wound in the opposite sense to the two inner ones, thus eliminating the effect both of uniform disturbances, and of non-uniform disturbances of constant horizontal gradient.

The complete system used is sketched in Fig. 7.7. The two outer coils are identical to the two inner ones and connected in series

with them but in the opposite sense. Consequently a *change* in the
earth's field (e.g. the diurnal variation) produces equal and opposite voltages in each set and the net effect is zero. As in the case of
the upper magnet of the astatic pair, the outer set is comparatively
remote from the sample, and the reduction in sensitivity due to the
compensating coils is small. The symmetrical disposition of the
compensating coils with respect to the inner set eliminates also
the effect of changing non-uniform fields such as might arise from
passing cars, and consequently the apparatus can be used in the
neighbourhood of a city. In contrast to the astatic magnetometer,
it is totally insensitive to *steady* external fields however spatially

(*Ph.*: Thomas-Photos, Oxford)

PLATE XXIV. Spinning magnetometer—cubic coil system. The sample is fastened
into a wooden box which fits onto a circular perspex table. This is driven at
300 rev/min by a vertical shaft, also of perspex.

non-uniform; nearby iron objects are objectionable only if subject to vibration.

Plate XXIV shows a different type of coil system, used at the Archæological Research Laboratory, Oxford. It consists of three coaxial sets, each comprising six square coils of the same size, this being 1 ft for the inner set, 2 ft for the middle set, and 3 ft for the outer set. Only two sets are used at any one time, the inner and the middle set for maximum sensitivity, or the middle and the outer set for maximum sample size. The advantage of the 'cubic' coil system is that a greater volume of uniform sensitivity is available for the same dimension of coil. This is achieved by winding different numbers of turns on the various members of the set (Rubens, 1945): for the middle set, of side 2 ft, the sensitivity is uniform to 1 per cent within a cube of side 1 ft. In this case the compensating coils are the outer set, wound with fewer turns, so that the product (area × turns) is the same for both sets. On account of the large size, the electric charge that flows on reversal of a moment of 1 emu is only 2×10^{-8} coulomb and it is necessary to interpose a d.c. amplifier between the coils and the ballistic galvanometer. A galvanometer photocell amplifier is convenient. The minimum detectable moment is 10^{-3} emu, the limit being dictated by Johnson noise in the coils and Brownian fluctuations in the primary galvanometer.

7.6.3 *Spinning Magnetometers*

In the previous case although the charge that flows during reversal depends only on the magnetic moment, the induced voltage in the coils is proportional to the rate of reversal. By rotating the sample continuously an a.c. voltage is induced; this can be more easily amplified and by restricting the frequency range to which the detector responds, electrical noise and the effects of extraneous disturbances can be reduced to a minimum.

For a fixed speed the induced voltage is proportional to the component of the sample's magnetization that lies in the plane perpendicular to the axis of rotation. By rotating the sample about three perpendicular axes in turn, the components in the corresponding planes are measured, and hence the magnitude and direction of the total moment can be deduced. In the case of the ballistic magnetometer the components in three perpendicular *directions* were measured; in the present case only the *plane* in which the component lies is known, and deduction of the direction of the total moment to within $\pm \frac{1}{2}°$ necessitates measurement of the components to better than ± 0.2 per cent. Consequently it is better to make a direct determination of the direction.

One method of doing this, employed by Thellier, is to mount two small coils on the rotating table, their axes perpendicular and in the plane of the table. Direct current is fed to each coil *via* slip-rings on the shaft driving the table. The current in each coil is adjusted until the resultant magnetic moment is exactly equal and opposite to the component of the sample in the plane of the table; this condition is indicated by zero voltage in the pick-up coils. Accurate measurement of the current in each annulling coil then gives the components of the sample's magnetization in two

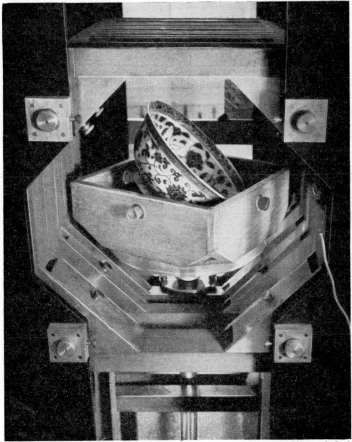

(*Ph.:* Thomas-Photos, Oxford)

PLATE XXV. Spinning magnetometer. For small specimens which are weakly magnetized, an inner set of coils (of side 1 ft) are mounted within the system shown in Plate XXIV.

perpendicular directions in the plane of the table. The procedure is then repeated with a different plane of the sample parallel to the plane of the table—which is horizontal. In this way both the magnitude and the direction of the sample's magnetization are accurately determined.

Considerations of the centrifugal force experienced by heavy samples limit the speed of rotation to 5 c/s (300 rev/min). At this frequency the output voltage from the pick-up coils is very small even before the annulling coils are energized. To obtain an accurate null position the pick-up coils are connected to a high-gain selective amplifier which feeds a 5 c/s vibration galvanometer. In this way extraneous signals picked up by the coils are eliminated and the effect of Johnson noise from the coils is kept to a minimum.

The system used at Oxford (Harold, 1960) is similar (see Fig. 7.8), except that the sample signal is annulled by means of mag-

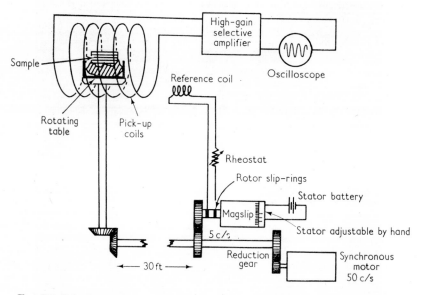

FIG. 7.8. Spinning magnetometer. The amplitude and phase of the 5 c/s signal fed to the reference coils are adjusted until the signal from the rotating sample is exactly cancelled. Plate XXIV shows the pick-up coils, which discriminate against outside interference.

netic linkage between a reference coil and the pick-up coils. This reference coil is fed with a 5 c/s signal derived from a 'magslip'* driven by the rotating shaft that turns the table. The amplitude

---

* In principle this consists of rotating coils in which a sine wave is generated by a stationary electromagnet.

and phase of the reference signal are adjusted until a null is indicated by the high-gain amplifier as before. Phase adjustment is obtained by altering the angle of the stator of the magslip; its setting is read directly from a vernier scale. This is calibrated with respect to direction on the table by means of a magnetized needle.

Spinning magnetometers are also widely used in 'rock magnetism'. Here the smaller sample size permits much higher speeds of rotation—often obtained by means of an air-turbine.

7.7 Results

7.7.1 *Declination and Dip*

The accuracy that can be attained under good conditions is illustrated by the measurements (Thellier and Thellier, 1951) on samples from a Roman kiln (*ca.* A.D. 300) at Carthage—one of the first structures ever sampled for archæomagnetism. The individual values of declination and dip respectively were:

0°30′ W, 50°45′	0°15′ W, 52°0′
2°15′ W, 50°30′	0°15′ W, 50°30′
3°45′ W, 49°45′	1°15′ W, 51°0′
2°15′ W, 50°15′	1°30′ W, 51°45′
1°45′ E, 51°15′	

The average values are $D = 1°15'$ W, $I = 51°0'$. For two Punic kilns, contemporaneous with the sack of Carthage by the Romans and therefore well-dated as 146 B.C., the average values were $D = 0°30'$ W, $I = 58°0'$.

The average specific magnetization of the samples from the Roman kiln at Carthage was 6×10^{-4} emu/g. For a Roman kiln near Trèves this figure (Thellier and Thellier, 1952) was 26×10^{-4} giving rise, due to local field distortion, to a wider spread in the individual results for D and I:

3°30′ W, 59°0′	3°45′ W, 60°0′
5°15′ W, 57°0′	9°45′ E, 62°30′
0°45′ W, 60°15′	5°30′ E, 59°45′
0°0′, 62°45′	4°0′ W, 61°30′
1°0′ W, 63°15′	0°30′ W, 62°0′
1°0′ E, 61°30′	2°0′ W, 62°15
0°0′, 63°0′	2°45′ W, 62°45

Nevertheless sufficient samples were taken for the average values to be reliable: these were $D = 1°$W, $I = 61°15'$. This kiln was dated archæologically to the latter half of the fourth century A.D. The present-day values for Trèves are $D = 5°$W, $I = 64°45'$, and for Carthage (Tunis), $D = 3°30'$ W, $I = 52°$. The two sites are rather far apart (900 miles) for comparison of results to be valid; nevertheless the change in I between the fourth century and the present day is about the same for both. A comprehensive range of data from structures in France, North Africa, Germany and Britain is shortly to be published by Thellier. It will then be possible, within those regions and over the periods of time covered, to use this information to establish the age of structures of unknown date.

A wide range of preliminary measurements has been made by Cook and Belshé (1958) on structures mainly in the eastern half of Britain. In many cases only a few samples were obtainable from a given structure and consequently the results must be treated with some reserve. Another difficulty in obtaining valid calibration points is uncertainty about the archæologically-derived date. It is often many years before the examination of the archæological evidence from an excavation has been completed and published, and even then dates are subject to revision as further comparable material comes to light. The number of structures excavated each year which are both well-dated archæologically and suitable for magnetic sampling is very limited; consequently it takes a long time to build up a reliable calibration curve. Nevertheless it seems well established that in Britain during the first four centuries A.D. the angle of dip decreased from about 70° to 63° and that in the middle of the fourth century the declination was about 3° West. Further measurements are in progress in Britain by groups from both Oxford* and Cambridge. The latter have also obtained samples from structures in Greece and North Africa, and the former from Cyprus.

According to Fig. 7.1, the maximum rates of change are 20° per century for declination, and 4° per century for inclination. It appears that during the Roman occupation of Britain the changes were much slower. Consequently, although this period is rich in baked material, it is by no means the ideal one for magnetic dating, and the method should be more valuable in other periods once sufficient structures of known date have been excavated.

A non-archæological source of information in some regions is lava from volcanic eruptions, although the possibility of distortion of the magnetic direction by the magnetism of the volcano itself must always be borne in mind. Chevallier (1925) has derived the following values for Sicily from measurements on Mount Etna:

1284 A.D., 7°E, 50°;	1566 A.D., 12°E, 52°;
1329 A.D., 10°E, 59°;	1669 A.D., 9°W, 63°;
1381 A.D., 17°E, 53°;	1911 A.D., 7°W, 47°.

* Tentative results include the following: 600(± 100)B.C., 10°E, 64°; 1080 (± 20) A.D., 4°E, 63°; 1130(± 10) A.D., 7°E, 52°; 1300(± 30) A.D., 6°E, 57°; 1325 (± 25) A.D., 3°W 53°; 1335(± 15) A.D., 8°W, 60°.

Directly recorded values are available as a check of the last three pairs and except for the value of dip for 1566 the agreement is reasonable.

In quoting the average values of D and I for a structure it is usual to express the likely error in terms of the 95 *per cent circle of confidence*. This is derived from statistical analysis (Fisher, 1953) of the individual variations of the direction of magnetization from sample to sample. If the 95 per cent circle of confidence (often referred to as 'the Fisher index at the 5 per cent level of significance') is quoted as θ degrees, this means that there is a 95 per cent probability that the true vector direction of the magnetization lies within a cone, of semi-angle θ degrees, coaxial with the vector direction defined by the values of D and I quoted. For $I \sim 60°$, the corresponding error in D is a little less than $\pm 2\theta$ degrees while for I the error is a little less than $\pm \theta$ degrees. The 'Fisher indices' computed for the quoted data for the kilns at Carthage and Trèves are 0·8 degrees and 1·3 degrees respectively.

A common feature of the curves shown in Figs. 7.1 and 7.2 is the clockwise motion of the representative point. Assuming the secular variation to result from near-surface disturbances of currents in the earth's core which drift slowly with respect to the crust, the motion will be clockwise if the drift is westward and anticlockwise if the drift is eastward. Hence the clockwise motion over the past few centuries is in agreement with the observed present-day westward drift of the large-scale magnetic disturbances mentioned in Section 2.2.3. Consequently it is of interest to know whether the motion of the representative point has been clockwise for all periods; if not, then one interpretation will be that the relative drift between core and crust has reversed.

7.7.2 *Intensity Measurements*

Table 7.1 gives results obtained in Paris (Thellier and Thellier, 1959) employing the thermal remagnetization technique (see Section 7.5.5). Particular attention was given to checking the magnetic stability during heating and to the validity of past values deduced for the field intensity. Most of the samples (about 40 in all) were bricks and the spread of values obtained from individual samples of the same set was of the order of 20 per cent; the average for each set should be accurate to within a few per cent.

The sets originated from sources up to a thousand miles apart, but since the remanent value of I was measured for each set, Thellier has been able to normalize the results to $I = 65°$ (the present-day value in Paris) using the relation

$$F_0 = \frac{2M}{R^3\sqrt{(1+3\cos^2 I)}} \qquad (7.5)$$

Table 7.1. Time variation of the earth's magnetic field intensity (after Thellier and Thellier, 1959, p. 354)

Place	Date	Ancient angle of dip (I)	Ancient field strength F_0	Type of measurement
Paris	1955	64°36′	0·464	Magnetic observatory
Paris	1930	64°35′	0·459	Magnetic observatory
Paris	1885	65°19′	0·463	Magnetic observatory
Paris	1848	66°45′	0·471	Direct measurement
Versailles	1750	74°0′	0·48	Remanent magnetism
Lille	1460	63°0′	0·56	Remanent magnetism
Paris	200	62°15′	0·70	Remanent magnetism
Bâle	175	63°30′	0·73	Remanent magnetism
Fréjus	200	60°30′	0·65	Remanent magnetism
Carthage	− 146	58°0′	0·71	Remanent magnetism
Carthage	− 600	—	0·76	Remanent magnetism

N.B. Although the field in Paris has increased between 1930 and 1955 this does not imply that the direction of change has now reversed. Analyses covering the whole surface of the earth indicate that between 1922 and 1945 the representative magnetic moment of the earth decreased by 1 per cent (Thellier and Thellier, 1959, p. 357).

This assumes that the earth's field is identical with that due to a hypothetical bar magnet of moment M, at the centre of the earth (of radius R). The result of the normalization is shown in Fig. 7.9; a steady, almost linear decrease of F_0 extending over the past 2000 years, and probably over the past 2600 years (the point for 600 B.C. could not be normalized as the value of I was not available).

If the samples leading to the high values of F_0 had carried an abnormally high value of I then it would be possible to explain the effect as a tilting of the earth's magnetic axis as a whole (i.e. the proximity of the magnetic north pole to the region of measurement), the actual moment, M, remaining constant. This is clearly not the case, but, before accepting that the decrease found represents a decrease in M, measurements are necessary over a more extended area of the earth's surface, for there is the possibility that the effect was a localized one. However, the changes are some-

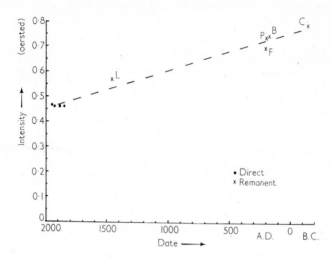

FIG. 7.9. Past intensity of earth's magnetic field (after Thellier and Thellier 1959, p. 354). The results have been normalized to Paris ($I = 65°$) by the dipole approximation, using the remanent angle of dip. Actual localities of samples are indicated by letter: B–Basle, C–Carthage (Tunis), F–Fréjus, L–Lille, P–Paris.

what greater in magnitude than observed in the various regional disturbances existing today.

Thellier extended his work further back in time by applying the technique to natural clay baked by contact with molten lava and to volcanic rock (andesite). The geological periods concerned were the middle and upper quaternary respectively. On account of instability on reheating and wide variation of values obtained from different samples, the results are doubtful, but they suggest that during the periods concerned the earth's field intensity was *less* than the present-day value.

The implications of a changing magnetic intensity for radiocarbon dating are discussed in Section 6.4.1. It is relevant to note here that the doubts as to the validity of the magnetic measurements expressed by Atwater and Ellickson (1958) appear to arise from a misunderstanding of the technique employed; the additional checks suggested by Cook (1958) are therefore redundant.

6+

7.7.3   Declination and Dip in Japan

A mammoth study of samples from kilns, furnaces and hearths extending from 3600 B.C. to A.D. 1600 has been carried out by Watanabe (1958, 1959). Altogether 1378 samples were measured, representing 55 different sites. Unfortunately only one site is well-dated archæologically; to obtain a calibration curve Watanabe assumes a regular time variation of I which is not inconsistent with the broad limits of the archæological chronology. Also used by Watanabe are five points from samples of volcanic lava measured by Nagata and Kato; these are well-dated by written records of the corresponding volcanic eruptions.

Magnetic samples from two prehistoric sites were relatable to radiocarbon dates. At one site the charcoal concerned was lying on top of the baked floor of a dwelling pit which had been destroyed by fire; the radiocarbon date obtained was 2600 ± 220 B.C. and the remanent magnetic directions (reduced to Tokyo) from a set of samples from the baked floor, were $D = 5 \pm 5°$ E and $I = 49 \pm 3°$. In the second case, the magnetic samples were only associated with the radiocarbon date *via* common pottery types found on two different sites; the date was 3150 ± 400 B.C. and the remanent declinations from five sets of samples varied between 4° E and 6° W, and the inclinations between 48° and 51°.

7.7.4   Dip Measurements on Chinese Yuëh Pottery

There is historical evidence that the green-glazed stoneware and proto-porcelain known as Yuëh was made at kilns in the vicinity of Shanghai over the period 300 B.C. to A.D. 1000. Measurements, made at Oxford, on some 50 specimens confirm that the pots were baked on their bases; this had been expected because their heavy glaze would make it difficult for them to be stacked while in the kiln. Little is known by art historians about the number of centuries for which a given style persisted and it is hoped to obtain magnetic evidence about this by seeing whether or not different stylistic groups have different angles of dip. It is intended to measure 300 specimens in order to average out the effects of uneven kiln floors.

There is stylistic dating for two of the groups and preliminary measurements (Aitken, 1958) indicate a value of 34° for the second or third centuries B.C. and 46° for the tenth century A.D. The present-day value is 43°.

7.8 Palæomagnetism

In view of the secular variation of declination and dip, it is surprising at first sight that the direction of remanent magnetism in rocks can be used to trace past variations in the positions of continental structures relative to each other and to the earth's axis of rotation. However, the fundamental assumption is made that over several thousand years the *average* values of D and I correspond to the field of a short bar magnet at the centre of the earth aligned along the axis of rotation. With this assumption the average value of I found in a given geological stratum can be used to deduce the effective geographical latitude at the time when the rock cooled from the molten state, and from the value of D, various possible combinations of longitude and orientation can also be worked out. Sedimentary rocks, notably red sandstones, can be used, the remanent direction being acquired as the magnetic particles are deposited.

In some geological eras magnetic evidence from different continents suggests that these continents moved in unison. This is interpreted as *polar wandering*, i.e. movement of the axis of rotation with respect to the earth's crust as a whole. Relative movement between continents is termed *continental drift*. Results bearing out these possibilities have been reviewed by Runcorn (1959) and by Irving (1958).

The idea of continental drift did not originate from palæomagnetism but from palæoclimatic indications revealed by geological structure. Thus the geological evidence of glacial conditions in India, South Africa, and Australia, some 200 million years ago suggests that at that time those continents were closely grouped around the South Pole. Another form of evidence is the wind direction indicated by sandstone formed from wind-blown sand dunes ('aeolian sandstances'); examination of Permian sandstones in Great Britain suggests a prevailing wind from the east and this is not inconsistent with the palæomagnetic indications that during the period concerned Britain was near enough to the Equator to be within the wind-belt of the northern trade winds (Opdyke and Runcorn, 1959).

A striking phenomenon encountered in rock magnetism is that of *reversed* remanent magnetism. For some rocks the mechanism of acquisition of remanent magnetism is such that the moment acquired is in the opposite direction to the applied field; but in many others a genuine reversal of the direction of the earth's magnetic field is implied, i.e. magnetic north pole and magnetic south have interchanged. The process of reversal takes place quite quickly geologically speaking (probably in less than 10 000 years) and alternative directions last for the order of 500 000 years.

Naturally acquired remanent magnetism is not of interest archæologically except for that acquired by varved clays. As in sedimentary rock formation, the magnetic particles are preferentially orientated while in suspension prior to deposition, and since varved clays can be accurately dated by counting the annual layers (see 5.2) this could be a very valuable record. Unfortunately the remanent angle of dip appears to be influenced by factors other than the magnetic field direction. On the other hand, the declination is faithfully preserved as long as the deposition occurs from fairly calm water. Interesting results covering the period 15 000 to 5000 B.C. in New England have been published by Johnson, Murphy and Torreson (1948), and measurements of Swedish varves in the periods 1100 B.C. to A.D. 750 and A.D. 1300 to A.D. 1900 have been made by Griffiths (1957).

References

Aitken, M. J., 1958: Magnetic dating–I. *Archaeometry* (Bull. Res. Lab. Arch., Oxford), **1**, 16–20

Atwater, H. A. and Ellickson, R. T., 1958: Remanent magnetization of ancient bricks. *Nature, Lond.*, **181**, 404

Bauer, L. A., 1899: On the Secular Variation of a Free Magnetic Needle. *Phys. Rev.*, **3**, 34–48

Blackett, P. M. S., 1952: A negative experiment relating to magnetism and the earth's rotation. *Phil. Trans.*, **250A**, 309–370

Chevallier, R., 1925: L'aimantation des laves de l'Etna et l'orientation du champ terrestre en Sicile du XII au XVIII siècles. *Ann. Phys., Paris*, **4**, 5–162

Cook, R. M., 1958: Intensity of remanent magnetization of archæological remains. *Nature, Lond.*, **181**, 1421–1422

Cook, R. M. and Belshé, J. C., 1958: Archæomagnetism: a Preliminary Report on Britain. *Antiquity*, **32**, 167–178

Fisher, R., 1953: Dispersion on a sphere. *Proc. roy. Soc. Lond.*, **217A**, 295–305

Folgheraiter, G., 1899: Sur les variations séculaires de l'inclinaison magnétique dans l'antiquité. *Arch. Sci. phys. nat.*, **8**, 5–16

Griffiths, D. H., 1957: The remanent magnetism of varved clays from Sweden. *Nature, Lond.*, **179**, 4549

Haigh, G., 1958: The process of magnetization by chemical change. *Phil. Mag.*, **3**, 267–286

Harold, M. R., 1960: Magnetic dating III—the spinning magnetometer. *Archæometry* (Bull. Res. Lab. Arch. Hist. Art, Oxford), **3**, 15–21

Irving, E., 1958: Palæographic reconstruction from paleomagnetism. *Geophys. J.*, **1**, 224

Johnson, E. A., Murphy, T. and Torreson, O. W., 1948: Pre-history of the earth's magnetic field. *Terr. Magn. Atmos. Elect.* **53**, 349–372

Néel, L., 1955: Some theoretical aspects of rock-magnetism. *Advances in Physics*, **4**, 191–243

Opdyke, N. D. and Runcorn, S. K., 1959: Palæomagnetism and ancient wind directions. *Endeavour*, **18**, 26–34

Rimbert, F., 1956a: Sur la désaimantation, par action de champs magnétiques alternatifs, de la magnétite et du sesquioxyde de fer α. *C. R. Acad. Sci., Paris*, **242**, 890–893

Rimbert, F., 1956b: Sur l'action de champs alternatifs sur des roches portant une aimantation rémanente isotherme de viscosité. *C. R. Acad. Sci., Paris*, **242**, 2536–2538

Rimbert, F., 1957: Sur l'aimantation rémanente anhystérétique des ferrimagnétiques. *C. R. Acad. Sci., Paris*, **245**, 406–408

Roquet, J., 1954: Rémanences magnétiques des oxydes de fer. *Ann. Géophys.*, **10**, 226–247, 282–325

Rubens, S. M., 1945: Cube-surface coil for producing a uniform magnetic field. *Rev. sci. Instrum.*, **16**, 243–245

Runcorn, S. K., 1959: Rock magnetism. *Science*, **129**, 1002–1012

Stacey, F. D., 1958: Thermo-remanent magnetization (TRM) of multidomain grains in igneous rocks. *Phil. Mag.*, **3**, 1391

Thellier, E., 1938: Sur l'aimantation des terres cuites et ses applications géophysiques. *Ann. Inst. Phys. Globe*, **16**, 157–302

Thellier, E., 1951: Propriétés magnétiques des terres cuites et des roches. *J. Phys.*, **12**, 205–218

Thellier, E. and Rimbert, F., 1955: Sur l'utilisation en paléomagnétisme de la désaimantation par champs alternatifs. *C. R. Acad. Sci., Paris*, **240**, 1404–1406

Thellier, E. and Thellier, O., 1951: Sur la direction du champ magnétique terrestre, retrouvée sur des parois de fours des époques punique et romaine, à Carthage. *C. R. Acad. Sci., Paris*, **233**, 1476–1478

Thellier, E. and Thellier, O., 1952: Sur la direction du champ magnétique terrestre, dans la région de Trèves, vers 380 après J.-C. *C. R. Acad. Sci., Paris*, **234**, 1464–1466

Thellier, E. and Thellier, O., 1959: Sur l'intensité du champ magnétique terrestre dans le passé historique et géologique. *Ann. Géophys.*, **15**, 285–376

Verhoogen, J., 1959: The origin of thermoremanent magnetism. *J. geophys. Res.*, **64**, 2441

Vestine, E. H., Laporte, L., Cooper, C., Lange, I. and Hendrix, W. C., 1947: Description of the earth's main magnetic field and its secular change, 1905–1945. *Publ. Carneg. Instn. (Dept. of Terrestial Magnetism)* No. **578**

Watanabe, N., 1958: Secular variation in the direction of geomagnetism as the standard scale for geomagnetochronology in Japan. *Nature, Lond.*, **182**, 383–384

Watanabe, N., 1959: The direction of remanent magnetism of baked earth and its application to chronology in Japan. *J. Fac. Sci., Tokyo Univ.*, **2**, 1–188

CHAPTER 8

ANALYSIS

8.1 Applications

In reporting archæological excavations great importance is rightly attached to precise visual descriptions of the objects unearthed. It is natural to extend such descriptions to chemical composition, but since the ordinary methods of 'wet' chemistry involve some degree of damage, and because of the labour involved, this is applied to only a small fraction of each group of similar objects. In this context analysis means the determination of those constituents which affect the general character of the object— essentially the major constituents, defined as those elements present to a higher concentration than 1 or 2 per cent. The multifarious techniques of chemistry are outside the scope of this book, and the present chapter is restricted to an outline of five analytical methods derived from physics, all of which are either non-destructive or only very slightly destructive. Three of these methods (Sections 8.3, 8.4, 8.5) permit the determination of minor constituents (1 per cent to 0·01 per cent) to an accuracy approaching that obtainable with ordinary chemical methods, and of *trace* elements (less than 0·01 per cent) in some cases. The other two methods (Sections 8.2 and 8.6) are of very specialized application.

Although the non-destructive aspect permits, in principle, the analysis of all objects excavated, the significance of the mass of piecemeal data so acquired would bear no relation to the cost of performing the analyses. To be digestible, analytic results must be obtained from well-planned and comprehensive programmes which —like present-day excavations—are designed to answer specific questions. An example of such a programme is the analysis of the pigment used in the decoration of some eighty pieces of Chinese blue-and-white porcelain by Young (1956), using an X-ray fluorescent spectrometer (see Section 8.4). This fine and valuable ware was made by Ming and pre-Ming potters over a period of several centuries, and variations, between contemporary pieces, in the quality of the colour had been ascribed to the use of imported cobalt ores for the more refined pieces, and the use of native cobalt ores for the less refined ones. The cobalt ores occurring in China, without exception, contain a high proportion of manganese, while those of Persia (the presumed source of importation) and the Middle East are manganese-free (Garner, 1956). Consequently it was possible to test the hypothesis that imported pigment was responsible for high quality by a restricted analysis, in which only the ratio of manganese to cobalt was measured, thereby enabling the whole programme to be completed in a dozen hours. No correlation was found. However, it was discovered that the use of imported ore is chronologically significant, its use ceasing by the end of the sixteenth century, and native pigment not being used until the beginning of the fifteenth (see Fig. 8.1). If the same

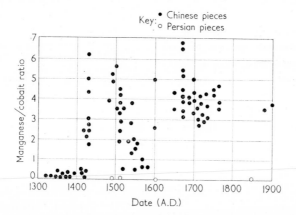

FIG. 8.1. Analysis of Chinese blue-and-white porcelain. The manganese/cobalt ratio in the blue pigment was determined with an X-ray fluorescent spectrometer. Native cobalt ore in China is rich in manganese and consequently a low manganese/cobalt ratio indicates the use of imported pigment.

amount of analytical effort had been put into complete analyses of fewer specimens it is likely that the main bulk of the elemental concentrations would have been uninterpretable and formed little compensation for the reduced number of specimens analysed.

*   *   *

The objectives served by analytical programmes may be broadly classified as : (*i*) information about techniques* ; (*ii*) information about date of production; and (*iii*) information about provenance.

The dating evidence obtained under (*ii*) differs from the methods

* Readers interested in the history of technology are referred to the exhaustive five-volume work edited by Singer, Holmyard and Hall (1954–1958).

158   PHYSICS AND ARCHÆOLOGY

of the last three chapters because in those, the time-varying property was external to the human race. Changes in the human race itself lead to dating, on an evolutionary scale, by measurement of skeletal remains (see Palmer, 1957, for instance). Habits and techniques change more quickly, and a particular type of pottery, for example, may be characteristic of a restricted span of years. This is *stylistic dating* which, like magnetic dating, needs some samples dated on other grounds in the first place. As we have seen in the example of the Chinese blue-and-white, analysis may reveal changes in composition that are not discernible to the naked eye; hence analysis may help to sub-divide stylistic periods or to link together different ones. Naturally objectives (*i*) and (*ii*) are closely interrelated, (*i*) usually being the primary goal.

In the Chinese blue-and-white example information was obtained about the provenance of the *pigment* rather than of the objects themselves. For economic reasons, it is to be expected that a potter will not work far from the source of his clay, so that the constituents of the baked-clay *body* of a pot may be characteristic of a given geographical region. This is the case for some major and minor constituents of Romano–British mortaria and colour-coated ware (Richards and Hartley, 1960) and this sort of information enables trade routes to be worked out. *Trace* elements can also have geographical significance in pottery (Sayre, Murrenhoff and Weick, 1958).

In the case of metal objects, geographically characteristic compositions are not to be expected as the general rule for several reasons. Firstly, metallic ores occur in geologically disturbed regions such that the impurity content is unlikely to be uniform even within the same working. Secondly, the refining process intervenes between parent ore and resultant metal. Thirdly, melting-down of old metal for re-use will tend to blur any distinguishing characteristics. Nevertheless, remarkable correlation has been found by Pittioni (1957) in Early Bronze Age material for which the supposed ancient workings are still extant in Austria. Derkosch, Mayer and Neuninger (1956), on the other hand, found difficulty in attributing copper objects of the late Stone and Early Bronze Ages to ore sites. Complex statistical methods have been used by Junghans and Sangmeister (1957) to divide the analyses of several thousand copper and bronze implements into twelve groups of differing average compositions; these groups have archæological significance both geographically and in terms of artefact-types. That such statistical groups have archæological significance even for re-used metal has been shown by Brown, Blin-Stoyle, Jolowicz and Humphreys (1959); their analysis of 500 British Middle and Late Bronze Age specimens indicated the deliberate addition of lead in the Late Bronze Age and showed that this could be used for distinguishing between material of the two periods. A general discussion of ancient metallurgical techniques has been given by Thompson (1958) who suggests that the general impurity level in copper and bronze reflects not only changing technical ability, but also, the gradual exhaustion of outcrop ores and the consequent use of deeper lying deposits which are less pure.

'Chemical dating' has been applied to Athenian bronze coin blanks (Caley and Deebel, 1955) and to Roman brass (Caley, 1955). The steadily decreasing zinc content of Roman brass, during the first two centuries A.D., is interpreted as continued preferential loss of zinc by oxidation and volatilization when old coins are melted down to make new ones. From the analyses (Emeleus, 1959) of several hundred early Greek and South Italian silver coins, Kraay (1959) has drawn various conclusions about trading connections, notably between Corinth, which lacked local silver mines, and Athens, whose mines at Laurium produced silver with a distinctively low impurity content of gold; evidence of deliberate debasements is also noted.

The composition of ancient glass has been exhaustively studied by Turner (1956); here, chronological variations in composition reflect changing techniques. Written record of the recipes used is sometimes available. The absence or presence of lead is a particularly striking characteristic of glass and glazes. The use of lead in pottery glazes is recorded in Mesopotamia in the seventeenth century B.C., but it was absent from glass of that period; nor was it used in Egyptian glazes until much later. A simple, non-destructive method for detecting lead—*beta-ray back-scattering*—is described in the last section of this chapter.

*   *   *

In general, random variations make large-scale programmes essential in order to establish, for a given type of object made at a given time and place, both the average composition and the limiting values. Even when such data has been obtained it must be used with caution in the attribution of objects of unknown origin, for although the composition corresponding to a certain place may appear to be unique, there may still exist unknown sources which invalidate this. In practice, too, limiting values often overlap, so that although the average composition for a group of similar objects may have significance, the analysis of any one by itself

6*

does not carry great weight. An exception is detection of fakes by an anomalous major constituent. In any case the importance of non-destructive methods remains paramount.

8.2 Density Determination

Mention of this simple method of determining the fineness of gold objects is warranted by its antiquity: Archimedes used it to detect the adulteration of the gold crown of Hieron of Syracuse. The object is weighed in air and weighed in water at a known temperature; the density is the weight in air divided by the difference of the weights in air and water. Since the density of gold is 19·3, the presence of quite small amounts of alloying components can be detected, as long as these are assumed to be silver or copper (densities 10·5 and 8·9 respectively) and the unlikely possibility of platinum (density 21·5) is ruled out.

The method has been discussed by Caley (1949) who shows that, because of uncertainty in the densities of the pure metals themselves, the likely error in determining the gold content is of the order of 1 per cent. This assumes that the alloying component is known and that no contraction or expansion occurs in alloying. If the alloying component is unknown, as is usually the case in practice, the method becomes semi-quantitative except for objects of high gold content; the uncertainty from this cause is less than 2 per cent as long as the gold content exceeds 95 per cent. Other sources of error are hidden cavities and foreign inclusions.

Caley (1949) has examined 50 ancient gold coins by this method, mainly of the Roman Empire, and a high degree of purity is evident—the majority contain more than 95 per cent gold. Such fineness is rare in naturally occurring gold and it indicates a highly efficient refining process.

8.3 Emission Spectrometry

If an electric spark passes between two metal electrodes, visible light is emitted; this results from excitation of the outer electrons of the atoms of the electrode material which has been volatilized by the heat of the spark. The light consists of a number of sharply-defined wavelengths which are characteristic of the elements that have been volatilized. If a parallel beam of light from the spark is passed through a prism, it is split up into its constituent wavelengths—in the same way that Newton first observed the optical spectrum of white light. The intensity of each wavelength present can be determined from the blackening of the respective lines produced on a photographic plate, and by comparison with standards of known composition, the concentrations of the elements in the electrode material can be found.

In practice it is unsatisfactory to use the material being analysed as electrodes, because the more volatile elements are favoured, and because only the surface layer is analysed. For the analysis of metals it is convenient to dissolve about 10 milligram of the sample in acid and to use the *porous cup* technique. In this, both electrodes are of graphite but the upper one is in the form of a cup, a few millimetres in diameter and a few millimetres deep. This cup is made porous by previous heating in a flame. When placed in the cup, the solution of the sample slowly seeps through the bottom, whereupon it is completely volatilized by the spark which is struck between the lower electrode and the bottom of the cup. An alternative, and better, method is to spray the solution into the spark.

For non-metallic specimens the sample (again about 10 milligrams) is ground to a fine powder and mixed with a flux (frequently a mixture of graphite and ammonium sulphate is used). This is placed in a carbon cup (non-porous) which now forms the lower electrode. A *d.c. arc* is struck from the upper carbon electrode and the sample is completely burnt away. Besides ensuring complete volatilization, the d.c. arc gives greater sensitivity, whereas the spark gives higher precision. Strictly speaking the arc spectrum is emitted by neutral atoms whereas in the spark, the atoms are ionized and the spectrum is more complex.

The spectrometer itself calls for high precision workmanship and is expensive (upwards of £2000). The prism is usually of quartz, and by using a light path of several metres extremely complex spectra are resolved into separate lines on the photographic plate. The blackening of each line is examined with a photometer (or *densitometer*) and the calculation back to concentrations in the sample is complicated. The use of standard samples of known composition is essential and these must resemble the actual composition of the specimen as closely as possible; this is because the efficiency of detection of a given element is affected by the presence of other elements.

The sample is obtained from metallic specimens by drilling a fine hôle (about 1 mm diameter) which can subsequently be disguised by filling with wax. For soft metals such as pewter, the specimen can be rubbed on a piece of glass from which the sample is subsequently recovered by acid treatment. For non-metallic specimens such as pottery and pottery glaze, chipping or scraping with a tungsten carbide knife is convenient. Except for coins, precious metals and fine pottery, the damage is not significant and the method can be described as *partially* non-destructive. Direct sparking to a metallic specimen itself, while suitable only for semi-qualitative analysis, limits the damage to a small pitting on the surface.

For routine work the concentrations of most minor elements can be determined to within a few parts per hundred. The minimum concentrations of trace elements (less than 0·01 per cent) that can be detected vary from element to element and depend on the major and minor constituents present; however, in many cases the lower limit is a few parts per million.

As examples of the archæological application of this technique the reader is referred to the following authors:

(a) *For the analysis of metals (excluding coins):* Oldeberg (1942); Otto and Witter (1952); Mayer and Machata (1953); Junghans, Klein and Scheufele (1954); Derkosch, Mayer and Neuninger (1956); Coghlan and Case (1957); Junghans and Sangmeister (1957); Pittioni (1957); Brown *et al.* (1959).

(b) *For the analysis of coins:* Cremascoli (1955), Allin and Wallace (1954).

(c) *For the analysis of pottery:* Sayre (1958); Richards and Hartley (1960).

(d) *For the analysis of glass and glazes:* Turner (1956); Stone and Thomas (1956).

8.4 X-Ray Fluorescent Spectrometry

Excitation of the inner electron shells of an atom results in the emission of X-rays, lying in the wavelength range 0·2 to 20 ångströms (1 ångström $= 10^{-8}$ cm). As with excitation of the outer electrons to give visible light, the wavelengths emitted are sharply defined and characteristic of each element. Separation of the radiation into its constituent wavelengths is accomplished by reflection from a *diffraction crystal*; in a crystal of quartz (for example) the spacing, d, between the planes of the crystal lattice is 3·34 ångströms, i.e. of the same order as X-ray wavelengths, and for a given wavelength appreciable reflection occurs only when the angle, θ, between the incident rays and the crystal face fulfils the relation

$$\sin \theta = \frac{n\lambda}{2d} \qquad (8.1)$$

where $n = 1, 2, 3,$ etc. Hence the constituent wavelengths of a beam

of X-rays can be determined by measuring the reflected intensity
for varying values of θ. The reflected X-rays can be detected by a
photographic plate, or more conveniently by a geiger counter,
gas-proportional counter, or scintillation counter.

The continuous spectrum of X-rays produced by a high voltage
(usually 50 kV) X-ray tube is used for excitation of the atoms in
the specimen; hence the term 'fluorescent'. Fig. 8.2 and Plate
XXVI show a typical experimental layout. The radiation emerges
from the X-ray tube through a thin beryllium window and is

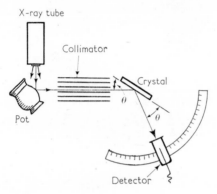

FIG. 8.2. X-Ray fluorescent spectrometer. Its most important archæological application is the rapid, non-destructive analysis of glass and glazes.

incident on the surface of the specimen at an angle of roughly 45°.
The characteristic fluorescent (or 'secondary') X-rays emitted by
atoms in the surface of the specimen can only reach the diffraction
crystal via a collimator, which sharply defines the angle θ between
the incident radiation and the crystal surface. Appreciable reflection occurs only when θ satisfies relation (8.1), and the detector
and crystal are orientated (by suitable mechanical gears) so that
both the collimator and the detector make the same angle θ with
the crystal face.

The concentration of a given element is determined by measuring the output of the counter when at a value of θ that corresponds
to an X-ray wavelength characteristic of that element. Each
element emits several wavelengths but the more important are the
$K(\alpha)$ and the $L(\alpha)$ radiations. The wavelength depends on the
atomic number, Z, and is given roughly by

$$\lambda_K = \frac{1200}{(Z-1)^2} \text{ ångströms} \qquad (8.2)$$

$$\lambda_L = \frac{6500}{(Z-7\cdot4)^2} \text{ ångströms} \qquad (8.3)$$

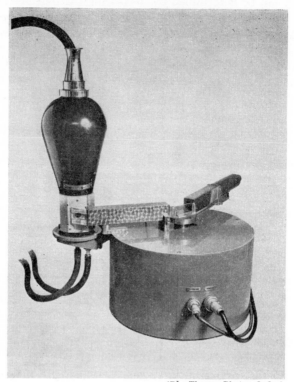

(*Ph.:* Thomas-Photos, Oxford

PLATE XXVI. X-Ray fluorescent spectrometer.
Left: X-ray tube
Centre: diffraction crystal
Right: detector
The sample is mounted against the perspex guides either side of the small
circular window at the bottom of the X-ray tube.

As for the optical spectrometer, calibration with standards closely
resembling the specimen is necessary.

Because X-rays are strongly absorbed by matter the analysis
relates only to a thin surface layer of the specimen. The thickness
of this layer is somewhat indeterminate but is of the order of 0·01
to 0·1 mm. Absorption in air also occurs and this limits the range
of elements that can be detected. Absorption increases rapidly
with increasing wavelength so that from equation (8.2) we see
that characteristic radiations from elements of low atomic number
will be most strongly absorbed. In practice the lower limit is
around $Z = 22$ (titanium). However, by enclosing the apparatus
in an atmosphere of helium, the absorption is reduced and the
lower limit falls to $Z = 13$ (aluminium). If the apparatus is placed

in a vacuum enclosure the limit can be further reduced, perhaps to $Z = 6$ (carbon). There is no upper limit to the atomic number of the element that can be detected as long as the lattice spacing, d, of the crystal is not too small. Besides quartz, lithium fluoride and sodium chloride are suitable.

The potential archæological value of this instrument is enormous because, except for a faint discoloration which disappears with time, it is entirely non-destructive. The positioning of the counter and recording of results can be made fully automatic so that the presence or absence of half-a-dozen elements can be checked in as many minutes. Quantitative comparisons between similar speci-mens are equally rapid but, as mentioned earlier, the reduction of these measurements to actual percentages requires calibration against standards and is somewhat involved. Because only the surface is examined, it is very suitable for the analysis of pottery glazes. For the same reason it is not satisfactory for metal analyses because of corrosion and surface enrichment effects. The sensitivity is not as great as the optical spectrometer; for routine work the lower limit is around 0·1 per cent for some elements, 0·01 per cent for others. In special cases 0·001 per cent can be reached.

The area of surface examined is about 1 cm across. This can be reduced by masking if it is desired to examine the detail of decora-tion, for instance. A development more suitable for this purpose is the X-ray microprobe (see Long and Cosslet, 1957); direct excitation by high-speed electrons is employed and the area covered can be reduced to 10^{-3} mm across by careful focussing. This instrument was developed primarily for the examination of alloy structure in metallurgy. An archæological application will be the study of surface enrichment of impurities in coins and metal implements by comparative analysis across a section cut through the surface.

A completely different method of X-ray analysis is X-ray *diffraction* analysis. In this the specimen must be in powdered form and the diffraction pattern produced when X-rays are passed through it can be interpreted in terms of the lattice spacings in the specimen. Thus the crystal structure is determined, permitting identification of the minerals present in pottery, for instance. This gives information both about the raw clay used and about the temperature of firing. Diffraction analysis has also been used in the detection of faked *patina* on bronzes.

For details of the technique of X-ray fluorescent analysis the reader is referred to the following authors: Friedman and Birks

(1948); Birks (1951); Parrish (1956); Hall (1957); Birks and Brooks (1958); Hall (1959); and for archæological applications to: Young (1956); Carroll (1957); Young and Whitmore (1957). An application of particular interest (Hall, 1959, p. 86) was the detection of chromium in the discoloration of the Piltdown skull, now supposed fake, suggesting the colour was due to an artificial stain rather than prolonged burial in ferruginous gravel.

8.5   Neutron Activation Analysis

With the two preceding techniques electromagnetic radiation (visible light and X-rays respectively) is emitted after excitation of the electrons of an atom. If the *nucleus* is excited a more highly penetrating form of electromagnetic radiation, gamma rays, may be emitted, and once again the wavelength is characteristic of the element concerned (in fact the method differentiates between different isotopes of the same element but this is not important for archæological applications). Excitation is most easily accomplished by *neutron activation*; the specimen is placed inside a nuclear reactor for a short period, and nuclear changes, produced in the constituents of the specimen by the intense slow-neutron flux (slow moving neutrons are more effective than fast), make the specimen weakly radioactive. After removal from the reactor, the gamma ray spectrum associated with this radioactivity is measured by means of a *scintillation spectrometer* (see Plate XXVII).

When gamma rays pass through a crystal of sodium iodide (containing a small percentage of thallium), flashes of visible light are produced. The number of flashes per second is proportional to the intensity of the gamma rays and the light energy contained in each flash is inversely proportional to the wavelength. The sodium iodide crystal (several inches in dimension) is placed in optical contact with a *photomultiplier* and carefully shielded from external light. The light flashes entering the photomultiplier fall onto a light sensitive surface and cause the ejection of electrons (i.e. the photoelectric effect utilized in ordinary photocells). A succession of *dynodes* multiplies these ejected electrons, thereby producing a sizeable electrical pulse at the photomultiplier output. The size of each pulse is proportional to the light energy contained in each flash from the crystal. By feeding the photomultiplier output, after amplification, into an electronic pulse analyser, the gamma-ray spectrum is determined. In discussing gamma rays it is more usual to refer to the energy carried by each gamma-ray photon rather than to wavelength. A wavelength of 12·4 Å corresponds

(*Ph.:* Thomas-Photos, Oxford)

PLATE XXVII. Gamma-ray spectrometer. A constant temperature enclosure to
the right contains the scintillation crystal and photomultiplier. The gamma-
ray spectrum is drawn out by the recorder as the single-channel pulse analyser
automatically scans through the energy range.

to a photon energy of 1 keV(1 keV equals 1.6×10^{-9} ergs).
The size of each electrical pulse entering the pulse analyser is
proportional to the energy of the gamma-ray photon from which it
originated. Hence the number of pulses of a given size per second
is proportional to the concentration in the specimen of the element
to which that pulse size corresponds.

The sensitivity varies widely between different elements but in
a number of cases trace impurities of only 1 part per million can be
detected. Some elements (e.g. lead) are not detectable at all either
because of insensitivity to neutron activation, or because the

induced radioactivity does not include gamma rays, but only beta rays (beta rays are emitted in nearly all cases). The energy spectrum of beta rays is not sharply defined and in general chemical separation is necessary for their utilization. With chemical separation extremely minute traces can be detected (e.g. 1 part in 10^{11} for gold), but for most archæological applications this aspect is irrelevant, since, if destruction of the specimen is permissible, analysis by the optical spectrometer is adequate.

Because it is entirely non-destructive (and the residual radioactivity is usually negligible), the technique is particularly applicable to coins and other precious objects. The whole volume of a coin is analysed since both neutrons and gamma rays are weakly absorbed in matter; for the same reason calibration is very much simpler, the sensitivity for a given element in general being independent of other constituents. There are two major drawbacks. Firstly, a nuclear reactor is required (although the activation from the neutron beam of a cyclotron or a linear accelerator is sufficient in special cases, e.g. Emoto, 1956). Secondly, the *resolution* of the gamma-ray spectrometer is poor. It is difficult to separate gamma-ray energies that lie within 10 per cent of one another, and consequently the method (without chemical separation—which involves destruction) is useless if gamma rays from many constituent elements are present. The advantage that can be obtained from differing radioactive decay times is limited, particularly if the composition is not known even qualitatively. Fortunately coins are of inherently simple composition and, except for special cases such as the determination of the copper impurity in a gold coin, the poor resolving power of the gamma-ray spectrometer is not serious. The drawback can be overcome by the use of *coincidence* spectrometry (see, for example, Ljunggren, 1960), at the cost of increased complexity.

A particularly easy application is the detection of plated coins; whereas the X-ray spectrometer responds mainly to the plating, the gamma-ray spectrometer responds to the body material as well and the analyses obtained by the two instruments are widely different.

Extensive application to the analysis of Greek silver coins has been made by Emeleus (1958) and Kraay (1959); for a summary of this work see Aitken *et al.* (1960). Coin analyses have also been made by Ambrosino and Pindrus (1953). Despite the difficulties of poor resolution, successful application to pottery analysis has been made by Sayre, Murrenhoff and Weick (1958), and on a smaller scale by Sayre and Dodson (1957) and Emeleus and Simpson

(1960). For the techniques of neutron activation analysis the reader is referred to Smales (1957), Atkins and Smales (1959) and Lenihan (1959); for gamma-ray spectroscopy in particular, see Koch (1957).

An interesting special application of neutron activation analysis was the investigation of whether a sixteenth-century Swedish king—Erik XIV—had been poisoned by mercury administered in a dish of pea soup. The detection of mercury in the royal remains suggests that this was in fact the case (Lenihan 1959).

8.6   The Beta-Ray Back-Scatter Meter

When beta rays (i.e. electrons or positrons) are incident on a specimen, some are absorbed but others emerge from the surface again. This 'back-scattering' is strongly dependent on the atomic numbers (Z) of the constituent elements, because the scattering arises from deflection of the electrons by the charge carried on the nucleus. The apparatus required to measure the relative back-scattering coefficient of a surface is comparatively simple and cheap to construct (about £30). A few microcuries of a suitable radioisotope, e.g. thallium-204 (half-life several years, beta-ray energy 0·76 MeV), provides the beta rays, and a Geiger counter detects the back-scattered intensity. The voltage for the Geiger is provided by a transistorized power supply and the counts per minute received by the Geiger are indicated by a transistorized ratemeter built into the same box (see Fig. 8.3 and Plate XXVIII).

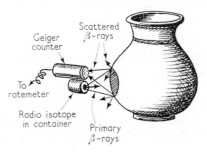

FIG. 8.3. Analysis by back-scattering of beta rays. For determining the lead content of glass and glazes.

The most useful application of the instrument is in detecting the lead ($Z = 82$) content of glass and glazes. The instrument is sensitive to the presence of 5 per cent or more of lead and it can be calibrated by reference to standards. The question to be answered is usually whether lead has been added deliberately, in which case the

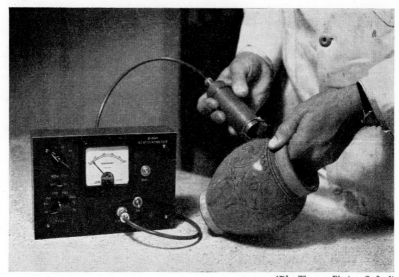

(*Ph.*: Thomas-Photos, Oxford)

PLATE XXVIII. Lead detection by beta-ray back-scattering

lead content is well above 10 per cent, or whether the glass is of a non-lead type—lead being entirely absent or present only as a trace impurity. Consequently the poor sensitivity is unimportant and more than compensated for by the portability of the instrument which makes it possible to establish whether a glass or glaze is lead or non-lead without removing the specimen from the museum shelf.

Two cautions must be borne in mind. Firstly, the presence of a high percentage of tin oxide (for tin, $Z = 50$) could simulate a low percentage of lead. Secondly, when examining glazes, the full sensitivity is not obtained unless the thickness of the glaze is at least one quarter of the range of the beta particles. The range of the beta particles (0·76 MeV) from thallium-204 is 1·2 mm (assuming the density is 2·5 gm per c.c), so that for thin glazes sulphur-35 is a preferable radioisotope as the beta-ray energy is only 0·167 MeV, corresponding to a range of 0·14 mm. In either case the strength of source necessary is too small to constitute a health hazard.

The technique has been used by Emeleus (1960) to measure the lead content of English glasses, glazes and pottery, and by Asahina, Yamasaki and Yamasaki (1957) on Japanese glass, porcelain and pigments. An interesting application by the latter authors was the determination of the thickness of the gilt on a

Buddha statue : since the base material had a low atomic number the scattered intensity was dependent on the gilt thickness ($Z = 79$ for gold), and calibration was obtained from gilt layers of known thickness.

References

Aitken, M. J., Emeleus, V. M., Hall, E. T. and Kraay, C. M., 1960 : Neutron activation analysis of ancient silver coins. *Radioisotopes in Physical Sciences (Copenhagen, Conference)*. RICC/37. Internat. Atomic Energy Authority, Vienna.

Allin, E. J. and Wallace, W. P., 1954 : Impurities in Euboean Monetary Silver. *American Numismatic Society Museum Notes* **VI**, 35–67

Ambrosino, G. and Pindrus, P., 1953 : Non-destructive analysis of ancient metal objects. *Rev. Métall.*, **50**, 136–138

Asahina, T.-I., Yamasaki, F. and Yamasaki, K., 1957 : Investigation of antique relics by means of beta-ray back scattering. *International Conference on Radioisotopes in Scientific Research, Paris* 1957, UNESCO/NS/RIC/64.

Atkins, D. H. F. and Smales, A. A., 1959 : Activation analysis. *Advance. inorg. Chem. Radiochem.*, **1**, 315–345

Birks, L. S., 1951 : Apparatus for vacuum X-ray fluorescence analysis of light elements. *Rev. sci. Instrum.*, **22**, 891–894

Birks, L. S. and Brooks, E. J., 1958 : X-rays lighten the analytical load. *Analyt. Chem.*, **30**, 19A–30A

Brown, M. A., Blin-Stoyle, A. E., Jolowicz, R. V. and Humphreys, C. C., 1959 : A sample analysis of British Middle and Late Bronze Age material using optical spectrometry. *Proc. prehist. Soc.*, **XXV**, 188–208

Caley, E. R., 1955 : On the existence of chronological variations in the composition of Roman brass. *Ohio J. Sci.*, **LV**, 137–140

Caley, E. R., 1949 : Validity of the specific gravity method for the determination of the fineness of gold objects. *Ohio J. Sci.*, **XLIX**, 73–82

Caley, E. R. and Deebel, W. H., 1955 : Chemical dating of bronze coin blanks from the Athens Agora. *Ohio J. Sci.*, **LV**, 44–46

Carroll, K. G., 1957 : Chemical analysis by X-ray fluorescence. *Amer. J. Archæol.*, **61**, 363

Coghlan, H. H. and Case, H., 1957 : Early metallurgy of copper in Ireland and Britain. *Proc. prehist. Soc.*, **XXIII**, 91–123

Cremascoli, F., 1955 : Spectrographic examination of ancient coins. *Sibrium*, **2**, 31–34

Derkosch, J., Mayer, F. X. and Neuninger, H., 1956 : Spectroscopic investigation of pre-historic copper finds. *Mikrochem. Acta*, 1649–1661

Emeleus, V. M., 1958 : Neutron activation. *Archæometry* (Bull. Res. Lab. Arch., Oxford), **1**, 6–15

Emeleus, V. M., 1959 : Some applications of neutron activation analysis and radioisotopes to archæological research. B.Sc. Thesis (unpublished), Oxford University

Emeleus, V. M., 1960 : Determination of lead content by beta-ray back scattering. *Archæometry* (Bull. Res. Lab. Arch., Oxford), **3**, 12–17

Emeleus, V. M. and Simpson, G., 1960 : Neutron activation of ancient Roman potsherds. *Nature, Lond.*, **185**, 196

Emoto, Y., 1956: Application of radioactivation analysis to antiques and arts and crafts. *Sci. Pap. Jap. Antiques*, **13**, 37–41

Friedman, H. and Birks, L. S., 1948: A Geiger counter spectrometer for X-ray fluorescent analysis. *Rev. sci. Instrum.*, **19**, 323–330

Garner, H. G., 1956: The use of imported and native cobalt in Chinese blue-and-white. *Oriental Art*, **II**, 48–50

Hall, E. T., 1959: X-ray fluorescence spectroscopy in chemical analysis. *Endeavour*, **XVIII**, 83–87

Hall, T., 1957: X-Ray spectroscopy. *Trace Analysis*, (Ed. Yoe and Koch), John Wiley, New York, pp. 458–491

Junghans, S. v., Klein, H. and Scheufele, E., 1954: Untersuchungen zur Kupfer- und Frühbronzezeit Süddeutschlands., *Bericht der Römisch-Germanischen Kommission* 1951–1953, Walter de Gruyter, Berlin, pp. 77–114

Junghans, S. v. and Sangmeister, E., 1957: Report on the progress of spectroscopic investigations of archaeological discoveries in Europe of the Copper and Early Bronze Ages. *Germania*, **35**, 11–18

Koch, H. W., 1957: Gamma-ray spectroscopy. *Trace Analysis*, (Ed. Yoe and Koch), John Wiley, New York, pp. 413–437

Kraay, C. M., 1959: Gold and copper traces in early Greek silver—II. *Archæometry* (Bull. Res. Lab. Arch., Oxford), **2**, 1–16

Lenihan, J. M. A., 1959: I.A.E.A. Symposium on Radioactivation Analysis in Vienna, June 1959. *Nature, Lond.*, **185**, 951

Ljunggren, K., 1960: Activation Analysis by means of Coincidence Spectrometry. *Radioisotopes in Physical Sciences (Copenhagen, Conference)* RICC/79.Internat. Atomic Energy Authority, Vienna

Long, J. V. P. and Cosslet, V. E., 1957: Some methods of X-ray microchemical analysis. *X-ray microscopy and microradiography* (Ed. Cosslet, Engstrom, Pattee), Academic Press, New York, pp. 435–442

Mayer, F. X. and Machata, G., 1953: Spectrographic series studies of prehistoric metal discoveries. *Öst. ChemZtg*, **54**, 178–179

Oldeburg, A., 1942: *Metallteknik under Förhistorisk Tid* (Lund 1942–3: Del I–II).

Otto, H. and Witter, W., 1952: *Handbuch der ältesten vorgeschichtlichen Metallurgie in Mitteleuropa*, Leipzig

Palmer, L. S., 1957: *Man's Journey through Time*, Hutchinson, London

Parrish, W., 1956: X-Ray spectrochemical analysis. *Philips tech. Rev.*, **17**, 269–286

Pittioni, R., 1957: Urzeitlicher Bergbau auf Kupfererz und Spurenanalyse. *Archæologia Austriaca*, **1**

Richards, E. E. and Hartley, K. F., 1960: Spectrographic analysis of Romano–British pottery. *Nature, Lond.*, **185**, 194–196

Sayre, E. V., 1958: Studies of ancient ceramic objects by means of neutron bombardment and emission spectroscopy. *Seminar Proceedings on Appl. of Science in Examination of Works of Art*, Research Lab. of Fine Arts, Boston, pp. 153–175

Sayre, E. V. and Dodson, R. W., 1957: Neutron activation study of mediterranean potsherds. *Amer. J. Archæol.*, **61**, 35–41

Sayre, E. V., Murrenhoff, A. and Weick, C. F., 1958: The nondestructive analysis of ancient potsherds through neutron activation. *Brookhaven National Laboratory*, Report BNL 508(T–122)

Singer, S., Holmyard, E. J. and Hall, A. R. (Eds.), 1954–1958: *A History of Technology*, Clarendon Press, Oxford, 5 vols.

Smales, A. A., 1957: Neutron activation analysis. *Trace Analysis* (Ed. Yoe and Koch), John Wiley, New York, pp. 518–545

Stone, J. F. S. and Thomas, L. C., 1956: The use and distribution of faience in the ancient East and Prehistoric Europe. *Proc. prehist. Soc.*, **22**, 37–84

Thompson, F. C., 1958: The early metallurgy of copper and bronze. *Man*, **LVIII**, 1–7

Turner, W. E. S., 1956: Studies in ancient glasses and glassmaking processes. *J. Soc. Glass. Tech.*, **40**, 39–52(T); 162–186(T); 277–300(T)

Young, S., 1956: An analysis of Chinese blue-and-white. *Oriental Art*, **II**, 43–47

Young, W. J. and Whitmore, F. E., 1957: Analysis of oriental ceramic wares by non-destructive X-ray methods. *Far east. Ceram. Bull.*, **9**, 1–27

AUTHOR INDEX

SUBJECT INDEX

The index has been restricted to items not easily traced from the Contents list at the beginning of the book. Heavy type indicates main entries